AT HOME WITH THE WEEDS:

A Memoir

Baleigh Bognar

"Nobody knows, a wildflower still grows
By the side of the road
And she don't need to need like the roses
She's at home with the weeds
And just as free as the night breeze"

-Bon Jovi, *Wildflower*

PREFACE

This is a story I have been aching to share for years.

I'm not claiming to write something you've never read before; it's nothing more than, unapologetically, my story. The story that has been tucked away inside my heart and my dreams for three years - you know the one, we all have one. The story that creeps up on you while you're driving with the windows down on your favorite back road. The story that tugs on your heart strings with the smell of a fresh rainfall or the smoke of a bonfire off in the distance. While, sure, it may just seem like one of those stories we all have, I *have* to share mine. This story deserves to be emblazoned on paper with the very essence of who I am spilling out from every word until you feel like you've known me your entire life and for some, like you are finally seeing me for the first time. Telling my story is how I keep it alive and luckily enough, the human experience allows us to relive a story as many times as we please. I wanted more.

I'm grateful to my body for allowing me to see the murky river and feel the heaviness of the summer air any time I dare to, but I want to paint that picture for the world, too. I want to physically hold my story and take it with me everywhere I go. I want to press my fingertips against the words that broke my heart and saved my life and feel each fiber of my being in every divot and curve of the letters.

I've always had the hardest time explaining my feelings in person but for whatever reason, I've always been able to spin a tapestry of my life with the written word. Maybe the process of writing about my experience will finally be the big exhale after years of holding it in with. Hell, maybe it will cause all my friends and family to throw me a big old-fashioned intervention. The possibilities are endless here. I'm willing to take that risk.

Regardless of what may come from this book, I could not be more excited for it. I am so ready to peel back the layers and make the world ugly-cry from the stench because that's how this story goes. It's beautiful, it's ugly, it's funny, it's gut-wrenching and it's truly amazing. I'm so excited to give it back to the world and experience it a million different ways through the eyes of each and every person who reads it. This story is the entirety of my heart - remember that as you experience it on your own.

We are diving head-first into this mess and it's going to hurt a little. That sounds intense, I know, but it's not a scooter-to-the-ankle kind of pain. It's the pain of your favorite tattoo; pain you would go through again in a heartbeat just to relive the first time you saw it all inky and swollen in the shitty lighting of the silvered tattoo-shop mirror. You know, just unexplainably and completely worth it.

1

The day I was admitted to the psych ward, or as adults call it, New Hanover Behavioral Health Hospital, began like every other day that week - with an iced cold brew coffee and an overwhelming sense of panic frothing in my throat. It's the breakfast of champions, and idiots alike. Sitting at my desk in my old office chair, I could have sworn my skin was trying to reject my heart and push it out through my chest. After I flew out of work with my breath stuck in my chest and my palms sweating uncontrollably, I immediately drove myself to the emergency room where I had been a frequent flyer this week. This was my third time there within seven days.

I have been dealing with anxiety and panic attacks since I was 12 years old, but at the ripe old age of 24, I was forced to realize that I no longer had it "under control." I had outgrown my childhood medication and gone through too much trauma with not nearly enough therapy to make sure I safely managed it. For me, a panic attack looks like sweaty palms, hiding out in the bathroom, chattering teeth, rocking and doubling over from sharp stomach pains, and in extreme cases, hyperventilating until I pass out. Luckily, the fainting stopped in middle school, however, the mental-stability hiccups did not.

This most recent break in mental stability was about six months in the making. I had been dating a marine on and off for about five years. We went to middle school together, graduated together, and went to three funerals together in which we both relied entirely on one another to keep each other standing during the service. I've learned now that it's impossible to keep the flames of love alive in a hurricane of desperation. Things afterwards were so dark, including the breakup, that my body said "Baleigh, we can't carry this any longer" and just stopped functioning altogether.

I felt responsible for my ex's well-being and that everything I did would affect it in some way or another. My mother was upset with me for the breakup, my best friends lived 11 hours away, and my coworkers didn't understand me. I was trapped with my anxiety and had no one to confide in. My guilt was a constant state of torture for me and now, it had begun to spill out between lips, and I no longer had the energy to keep it in.

I paced back and forth in the parking lot of the ER for three hours because I knew I couldn't afford another visit. That really eased my anxiety though, knowing I couldn't afford to have a panic attack. I could only imagine what the patients, doctors, and visitors of the third floor were thinking from their vantage point; A tall, painfully pale, and incredibly disheveled young woman slowly making her way up to the entrance doors only to turn right around and dejectedly walk back to her old black Sonata. With my long dark hair that I kept tied up in a scrunchie that was all but a rubber band and the last few strong-willed strands of fabric I'm sure I could've passed for a street beggar who's make-shift tent was somewhere blowing around on Front Street.

I called my best friend Silvy, my mom, God himself, and anyone who I thought could calm me down but to no avail. I dragged myself through the automatic doors and got in the triage line. They knew why I had come back so I took my usual seat in the waiting room, facing the door so I could watch the nurse come out and call my name. You never know what you're going to get when you sit down in an ER waiting room chair. You could be there for minutes or hours. This waiting, as you could imagine, only heightens the panic attack because the anticipation of when you will be the lucky winner whose number gets called next, is unbearable. I never make eye contact with anyone because it feels like an admission of my mania. I like to keep my "crazy" to myself for as long as I can and then I dump it all on the doctor, who I like to assume, has seen much, much worse.

We flew through vitals; I had no fever, my blood pressure was fine, and my heart rate was terrifyingly high, but that was the usual. I shivered and shook in my Ugg boots while I waited for her to take me back to a room. My teeth were chattering so hard, and my jaw was clenched so tight that I was having trouble getting my words out. I knew this particular panic attack was going to be one to tell the grandkids about some day.

As the nurse took me to my room, all I could mutter was "Please. Please hurry with the doctor." Poor thing, I could see in her eyes that she was thinking *Bless her heart, she thinks she's next to see the doctor* but what she said was "The doctor is busy today, he'll be in as soon as he can, don't worry." *My ass,* I thought.

I texted my mom as my panic heightened with each ticking second. My eyesight was beginning to blur with the lack of oxygen and the overdose of adrenaline coursing through my trembling body. I was blinking just as rapidly as I was breathing, and I was gripping the triage chair so tightly that I was beginning to rip the cheap leather. I was past the point of return, there was no coming out of this without a giant needle full of Ativan shoved in my right butt cheek to knock me out and even then, I knew I would be back again tomorrow. (I've always thought that patients with panic disorder should have a rewards card for the ER. Something along the lines of a punch card; every third visit is free! But I digress.)

I decided that the nurse must not have realized I was obviously dying, and I punched the call button with my clenched fist. "I'm sorry, I really need someone to come help me, I can't do this anymore and I'm really scared." Rule number one of having a panic attack: Always apologize to the medical staff for having a panic attack.

"Okay honey we're coming, just hold on," she said. I have to say, having a panic attack in the south is pretty nice. All the nurses call you honey or baby, even when they hate you.

As the minutes ticked by, I knew they weren't coming. Now all I could think was *I'm at the ER and even they can't help me. If they can't help me, who can? How will I ever make this feeling stop?* And that put me over the edge. I was gripped with this irrational thought that if someone didn't help me soon, I would have to die if I wanted to feel better. This is the rationale your brain uses when in the throes of a five-hour panic attack, "death is the only way out!"

I continued to text my mom despite promising myself I would never scare or worry her with my panic attacks again; it was already hard for her to live in Ohio, 11 hours away from her only child. But it was my last resort; I felt this was all I could do to keep myself alive at this point.

"Mom, this one's really bad. I'm scared. I

don't want to die, not at all, but I'm scared there's no other way to make this panic and terror go away. Please come down. I'm so sorry."

I hated that I had to get my mom involved but I knew she was the only one who could help me at this breaking point. Whether she responded to my text or not, I knew she was coming. No questions asked.

It wasn't long after I sent that text that I was admitted to the behavioral health wing of the hospital. Under normal circumstances, this would have terrified me but in that moment, I felt nothing but relief. I was finally going to have professionals to hand my giant pile of terror over to so that I would no longer have to carry it around with me day in and day out like an oversized tumor. The ER nurses then immediately drugged me up and I faded in and out of sleep for a few hours until they finally found a bed for me at 3 a.m. I vaguely remember speaking to a psychiatrist but all I remember telling her is "I don't want to die; I just can't figure out how to live."

When they woke me up to take me to the Behavioral Health wing, I was given a blanket and a quick run-down of what was going to happen next. First, there were a lot of things that weren't allowed in the behavioral health unit - if you had to ask, the answer was probably no. When I arrived, they took my purse, cellphone and clothes. If you're picturing intake at the county jail, I'm painting you a valid picture.

Patients are given a weird hospital gown/pantsuit situation until you're assigned to your room. Once you get to your room, you can put your clothes back on, but not until each piece of clothing is fully inspected for "hazardous" items such as pins, buckles or zippers. As I watched them cut the strings out of my favorite hoodie and my Cleveland Browns sweatpants, all I could think of were the bleach stains on my pants and how mad I still was at Silvy for lying a cracked bottle of bleach on my pile of freshly cleaned clothes all those months ago. The staff explained to me that they were cutting the strings out of my clothes, so I don't use them to potentially hang myself. I focused harder on the bleach stains.

I had to be quiet while putting all my stuff away in my shared room because my roommate was asleep. With her foghorn of a snore, I doubted anything I was doing would even register with her, so I clumsily fumbled around in the dark until I found the sad little wooden toothbrush I was given when I checked in. It took everything in me to keep my eyes open while I brushed my teeth and washed my face. I was so tired from the long night, the drugs, and the panic attack. I passed out seconds after hitting the paper-covered pillow and began the best 3-day sleep of my life.

I woke up the next morning on that rubber mattress and I was drenched in sweat with my earplugs haphazardly hanging from my ears. I slept like a rock with the peace of knowing that I was finally in a safe place full of people who could take care of me and help me fend off the monsters that danced behind the bushes and trees in my head. I knew that I was finally going to get the help I've needed for years. No more excuses of not being able to afford it or knowing where or how to get it. It was now a necessity when really, it should have always been one. I knew I wasn't in the behavioral health unit of this North Carolina hospital because I wanted to die, I was there to re-learn how to do what "normal" people do by instinct-stay alive.

So, I did what I was told; I woke up for vitals, I woke up for lunch, and I showered every day. However, lunch always got me in trouble. Everyone knows the only perk to depression and anxiety is that you lose weight, right? Wrong. Turns out doctors and nurses don't allow for unhealthy eating patterns and inadequate nutrition in hospitals. Who knew? The patients here had to turn in their food tray at the end of every meal to prove that they were eating. I hadn't yet learned that trading your food items was the loophole to this system when I stood up to turn in my food tray that first day.

"Name?" the nurse asked.

"Baleigh. Baleigh Bognar" I replied.

"Yes, here you are. Mmm, didn't eat much

today. You need to start eating more of your meals," the male nurse reprimanded me.

He sounded bored by the fact that my tray was still completely untouched, this must not be his first rodeo. This nurse happened to be on lunch-tray duty every day and I don't think he ever realized I was the same girl as the day before with the full tray. He repeated: "Mmm, didn't eat much today. You need to start eating more of your food" every single time. I wondered if there were ever any real repercussions to not eating or if the staff had just stopped bothering to try. It's hard to have an appetite when you're at rock bottom but it's even harder to entice someone at rock bottom to eat, I suppose.

I took up the role of "loner-girl" in the behavioral health pod. I spent most of my time sitting alone in my room or on the sagging couch in the common area observing the others while I waited for my turn for vitals. There was one girl there, probably a teenager, who was visibly covered head to toe in scars. Her arms, legs, stomach, every inch had been sliced at in one way or another. She was the ringleader of the pod. The Regina George, as I referred to her. She played the shitty board games as loudly as she could and with just as much grandeur while the others laughed and praised her. She showed off her scars like prized tattoos, always lifting her shirt to scratch her stomach or sweep her arms out in wide gestures while titillating the others in her clique. I couldn't understand why someone as bubbly and lively as her would carve herself up like a Thanksgiving turkey in her free time; it was horribly depressing.

Then there was Etta. I never learned what her real name was, but Etta seemed to fit her nicely. Etta was probably in her sixties or seventies, a small and frail woman with short white hair. Everything about her screamed "I'm trying to disappear, but they won't let me." She was the saddest woman I had ever seen, and it broke my heart to look at her sometimes. She walked the common area all day clutching her tissues and quietly sobbing to herself. When she caught my eye in passing or at lunch, she would offer up the most pained and rueful smile in a way that suggested it felt obligatory of her. She could see right through anyone and convey that she understands you're hurting but was also apologizing for her own emotional state in that way older white women often do.

By the end of my first day there, I was on a mission to get out of the hospital. I was convinced that I didn't belong here with these people. I was not depressed like Etta, nor was I screaming to be seen by anyone (anyone at all) like Hot Topic Regina George. In my desperate attempt to get out of there, I rushed all my appointments with the doctors and psychiatrists and spent my free time making calls to my mom who was still stuck in the

Raleigh-Durham airport.

My phone calls with my mom consisted of hushed whispers about our plans to get me out of there as soon as possible. It was Prison Break, wife-beater tank tops and all. If I felt trapped in my mind before coming to the ER, it was almost worse now that I was *actually* trapped in this cold and sterile building. I was itching to be free again. The grass is always greener.

While I desperately wanted to be in my own bed again, I was also terrified to eventually go back to my tiny apartment by myself. I wanted nothing more than to be back home in Ohio with my family and I knew that I wouldn't feel better until that happened. I had to be somewhere that I felt safe and taken care of and could finally let my guard down. I needed to be surrounded by people that loved me and wouldn't judge me for who I really was or for my anxiety disorder.

After finally realizing that being back home was the only way to end this vicious cycle of ER visits and life-shattering panic attacks, I knew I would be leaving North Carolina as soon as they discharged me. This also meant there were a lot of doors that I needed to close to make that happen. I had to sublet my shitty apartment, finish my associate degree online, put in my two weeks' notice at work and look for a job in Ohio. The pang in my heart that began to throb at the thought of leaving my beautiful beach behind was daunting. I wondered if leaving Wilmington was a mistake, but I knew it had to be done. My time down here had come to an end, and I would cherish my Wilmington memories for the rest of my life, but Ohio was calling me home. There were many sad goodbyes ahead of me, but I knew the promise of being close to my mother again would get me through them all.

Thankfully, my mom would be landing in Wilmington International Airport soon. She was more than ready to get me the hell out of North Carolina and out of that hospital so she could take care of me herself. However, the nurses weren't impressed with my progress and were hesitant to let me leave yet. I stressed to them that being held against my will in an unfamiliar place full of strangers was only pushing me further over the edge, so they begrudgingly agreed to help me begin the discharge process early.

My mom picked me up from the hospital two days later and we sobbed in each other's arms in the lobby. Her tears were tears of relief that I was alive and that she was finally holding me. My tears were tears I had been holding in for days and didn't trust anyone else but her to wipe away.

After leaving the hospital, the rest of my short days in North Carolina were a blur of counseling sessions, doctors' appointments, homework assignments, apartment showings and phone call interviews. I was on autopilot for most of them because I knew I couldn't actually begin the healing process until I got home to Ohio where I could build a foundation of counselors and psychiatrists that I would see permanently rather than these temporary ones I was assigned to in Wilmington. I was just going through the motions until I could finally let my guard down back home up north.

I said my goodbyes to my lovely coworkers, my favorite beach access and my new-found friends. Out of all my goodbyes, none hurt quite like the long goodbye I said to Wrightsville beach. That beach has always felt like a second home and helped me through my hardest times in North Carolina.

Standing next to an ocean is like going to church for me. The ocean takes the mountains that I carry on my shoulders and makes them small enough for me to feel light again. It listens to my innermost thoughts with the same unconditional love found in God's heart. It gives me the forgiveness I don't feel I deserve, and it shows me to always keep going. The ocean takes you as you are and promises to always be there when you need to come back. I remember thinking *What if I never find anything like this in Ohio?* and trying as hard as I could to memorize every last miniscule detail of that beach access point. Part of my heart will always lie in the sand of that little beach.

My mom and I packed up the last of my things that would fit in my car, including my two cats, and headed for Ohio one last time. The eleven-hour drive home through the Appalachian Mountains (pronounced like 'App ul-latch-in' according to anyone who has ever lived in that area) was a bit of a blur as I panicked throughout the entire two-day endeavor. One of my triggers is not knowing where I am or where the closest ER is so traveling through the mountains in the dark was all but consuming me. I was fighting to hold it together the whole time.

Finally, my mom, my cats Sadie and Huey, and I pulled up to my mom's home in Ohio where I had spent my teenage years. Rather than feeling relieved like I had been expecting to feel, I felt complacent. The development had barely changed, and neither had the large colonial with its solid red door that loomed in front of me. I knew that up those worn carpeted stairs, my high school bedroom waited for me with the wine-stained mattress from years of unsuccessfully trying to hide alcohol from my parents. The cookie-cutter fenced-in yard, the pale lavender walls of the kitchen, and the familiar squeak of our old washer and dryer welcomed me at the door. It wasn't the same now that the family dog was gone but it still felt like home. It still smelled like safety, warmth, and nostalgia.

I couldn't shake the feeling of self-pity that came over me once I stepped inside. This was the third time now that I struck out on my own and came crawling back to the comfort of my mother's house after another failed attempt. *Back again,* I thought as I set my bags down on the hardwood floor.

At my feet, Sadie let out a questioning little meow as if to say "Really Mom? We're back at Grandma's again?" This made me feel defensive even though I was clearly just projecting my insecurities onto my poor cat who probably just really had to pee. With a dramatic sigh, I responded to my cat (that could not understand me, obviously) "I know I know, we're back. Again. This is the last time though Bubby, I swear" and for the love of the sweet sweet Lord above, I hoped I wasn't lying to her.

2

I can't say for sure but if I had to guess, I'd say I slept the entire first week I was home. Feeling safe and at ease for the first time in about a year makes for the world's hardest sleep. Being home with my mother after a long year of fighting with my own mind and being enslaved to my anxiety felt as comforting as a warm blanket draped around my shoulders in a cold ER. Things weren't 100% better, but there was a promise in the air of better days to come.

My mom has always been my safe place to land. I never met my father, so it was just the two of us for much of my life. As a child, I was very attached to my mother and would often cry when she left for work or dropped me off at preschool. I remember spending my preschool and kindergarten days mostly playing and sitting alone because there was no one other than my mother that I would rather play with. I couldn't wait until it was time for her to come back for me at the end of the day.

I am the spitting image of my mom, especially now with my thick blonde hair. To stand toe-to-toe with my mother is to look into a mirror. Both of us stood tall and skinny in our younger years and baby-faced as adults. We have the same sense of humor, but we differ in many ways religiously, politically, and aesthetically. There's not a shirt on this planet that my mom and I can both agree to liking.

When you grow up with an ER nurse for a mother, it becomes almost impossible to trust that there is anyone else in the world who can take care of you like she can. When I was 12 and passed out at school from my first panic attack, she was the nurse who had to give me a catheter to collect my urine sample. When I was 13 and got mono so bad that my throat blistered, she was the one who put my IV in at the ER. When I was 19 and got a basement tattoo on my hand that later got infected, she was also unfortunately the nurse who cleaned and dressed my hand. There was nothing my mother couldn't fix for me and there was no better treatment center than her grey chaise lounge sofa and her famous cheeseburger casserole. She had her work cut out for her this time, granted, but I never had a doubt in my mind that she couldn't fix me again now too.

Despite the best sleep of my life tucked deep under the covers of my teenage self's bright teal comforter, hibernation had to end, and counseling needed to begin. It was finally time to take care of myself the way my body and mind had been craving for years. I was on the medications that worked best for me thanks to the psychiatrists in North Carolina, now I just needed to get my brain to follow along with my body's new-found equilibrium. There were so many pamphlets, papers, instructions and phone numbers shoved into my arms when I left the hospital that I had no idea where to start. So, I decided to call my primary physician for some guidance because he is THE BEST (shout out Dr. Fantelli!)

Anyway, my doctor sent me to a nearby counseling center that he highly recommended and I could not wait to dive into therapy. It was something I had so desperately craved in North Carolina but could never afford. I couldn't afford my rent without the help of my family let alone anything extra. Now that I didn't have bills to pay at my mom's house, I could finally focus on getting better and making a connection with a counselor that genuinely wanted to help me. There was a light at the end of the tunnel, but it came with a hefty price tag, as these tunnel lights often do. This time, it was a price I was finally willing and able to pay.

Sometimes, to pass time in North Carolina, I would spend hours googling therapists, emailing their offices to see if they would work with me on prices, and reading the glowing reviews of counselors I could never afford but fantasized about working with. Help always seemed to be just out of reach for me and the guilt of "not trying hard enough" to find it would eat me alive at night.

I arrived at my first therapy session with a pocketful of hope and excitement. I couldn't wait to have all my lifelong problems that were strewn over the desk chairs in my brain and the lamp shades in my heart tied neatly into a bow by this promising new stranger. In a perfect world, maybe, but I didn't know that yet.

My counselor, we'll call her Margie, was as sweet as could be and that was exactly why I knew she was not going to work out for me. It was like handing a daisy to a gorilla and hoping they wouldn't crush it. Good lord did she try to get through it with me though. It started out promising - she was a yoga instructor and yoga was (and continues to be) my lifeline. I explained to Margie that this was not my first therapy rodeo. Since the age of 13, I had been to countless psychiatrists, counselors and therapists for my anxiety issues and panic attacks. She seemed to understand that until she said to me, and I quote:

"Have you tried breathing exercises?"

BREATHING. EXERCISES. I just gaped at her like a cartoon. I thought to myself, *Ma'am, you have been doing this for how long? I am not paying you $100 an hour to tell me to breathe. In fact, if I* *had a dollar for every time someone told me to just breathe, I could afford to pay you $100 an hour to tell me to just breathe.* I have tried so many different breathing practices, in yoga and counselors' offices alike, that my lungs should be used as a makeshift breathing apparatus long after I am dead. You begin to cultivate a sense of bitterness and jade after hearing the same advice for so much of your life. Give me something original here Margs.

For you lucky bastards who have never had a panic attack, the very first thing a doctor, counselor, yoga instructor, friend, or homeless man on the street will tell you is to take a deep breath. And yes, this DOES help some people but for the love of Eliza Thornberry I need more than that basic information from a counselor. It's like when your phone starts acting up and you call Verizon and they say, "Have you tried turning it off and turning it back on again?" and you have to have the power of Christ within you not to say, "OBVIOUSLY I ALREADY TRIED THAT CHAD."

I was now less than motivated to return to Margie's remarkably comfortable chic grey loveseat next week. It was heartbreaking to be so excited for some truly profound piece of advice that would make me go *Wow! How have I never realized this?! Of course, it's so simple, I'll feel so much better now!* I had set myself up for failure without realizing it by putting so much pressure on this one appointment and this one person who is ultimately only human. I thought I would be walking out of there feeling hopeful for the future and shedding the chains of my fear flawlessly like a Beyonce music video or something.

I put my disappointment aside and bellied up to Margie's stupid couch again anyway because Silvy said it would be good for me to stick it out and Silvy was always right, unfortunately. Maybe that was just Margie's day-one stuff that she had to tell me just in case, after thirteen years of having panic attacks, no one had suggested taking a deep breath yet. I went back for my next appointment, and it only got worse from there. What I wish I had known then was that Margie was just not the right counselor for me. In my head, I just assumed I couldn't be helped.

I knew she wasn't right for me because when I told Margie some of my gory life stories, she would literally gasp. Like her second job was re-cording theatrical sound effects and she used my sessions to practice her "shocked gasp." This gasp was usually followed with an "Oh my!" or a moment of her clutching her phantom pearl necklace. I just wanted to stop right in the middle of my stories and say to this poor fragile woman "Margie, please do not act disgusted when I tell you that I have never met my father and his daughter found me on Facebook. This is your job. Are you aware that you are supposed to be helping me?" By the way, we will get into the shit show that is my family history in the next book - there's no room for it in my favorite story of all time, sorry readers.

Anyway, it got to the point where I could feel myself physically wince before telling Margie a story from my life because I knew it was going to raddle her to hear it. Teacher becomes the student or whatever.

As they would say in the south: Bless her heart. Poor thing just shriveled up every time a swear word slipped out while I was reenacting a particularly touchy part of a story from my recent past. I know Margie really wanted to help me, but I was just too much for her. Abrasive, I believe is the correct word.

I'm too much for a lot of people, or so I've been told. I am painfully open and honest about the good, bad, and ugly parts of who I am and who I have been. I can't recall a specific time when someone has outright told me I'm too much, and that may even just be a self-fulfilling prophecy, but it's something I have always carried with me. It pains me to say this because it sounds so cliché and self-pitying, but I think in a way, I always felt like my father never came back for me because there was something about me that just wasn't lovable to him.

Then as my relationships began to fail, I would always chalk it up to that; I'm not someone a person stays with for too long because "I'm too much." I use my anxiety as a crutch sometimes. I convince myself that my panic attacks and inability to do basic things like get on a plane or go on a spontaneous adventure with friends without googling the nearest ER beforehand is why people always gracefully bow out of my life. I have a hunch that I'm really the one inadvertently pushing people away and using my anxiety to cushion the blow. Just a hunch though, not quite a fact yet.

I projected all these things on to Margie and became the patient that insisted on being rough around the edges, a handful, a rebel. I wanted her to dread our sessions, and I went out of my way to make my stories uncomfortable for her. It became yet another game of "Push or be pushed away."

Maybe she did genuinely feel sorry for the things I've been through and the stories I told her about my past. She's a therapist for God's sake, I doubt that little old me could be "too much" for her but that didn't stop me from trying. I used this reasoning to conclude that I wasn't "getting" anything from my sessions with Margie. I pushed her away so I could stick to my narrative of being too much for people. She wasn't a good match for me because I felt I had the power in our conversations, and I knew I could push her around but that wasn't entirely her fault.

In the meantime, while I was trying to figure out my new job, my mental health, my new yoga studio, a new journaling routine, and re-navigating how to live with my mom, step-dad, and step-brother again, I decided it would be a great idea to meet up with an old flame. I was craving a little attention outside of my support system. I wanted a break from being the broken girl, even if it meant lighting an empty candle.

You will learn quickly that I am a sucker for love. I love love, I want to find love everywhere, and I can find it in everyone. All the Libra ladies! It's a curse, and sometimes it's challenging to be grateful to be ruled by planet Venus, but we march on, loving love with our giant hearts, us Libra ladies. We daddy-issue disciples; burning for love while simultaneously destroying it before it can destroy us.

I've not had much luck with *relationships* in my life, but I've had a lot of luck with love. Relationships make love so complicated, and I think that's why I'm not so good at them. All the rules, the games we end up playing despite vowing to never play games, the expectations, the outsiders peering in via every social media platform Apple has to offer, that's what ruins love and distorts it into something you no longer recognize. It becomes so filtered, with dog ears and animated hearts, that one day you roll over and realize you don't really know the person lying next to you anymore. I would find myself wondering why my, now, ex-boyfriend had the nerve to change so much without me when we were supposed to cherish our love like a newborn until it could stand the test of time on its own two feet. *How dare you grow without me.*

When I fall in love with someone, really truly fall in love with someone, I expect the same in return and that's just not the way things are for everyone. I want that "honeymoon" stage forever and I panic when it starts to fade and that's when the self-sabotage begins.

I get so discouraged when people are quick to tell you that the honeymoon stage doesn't last long at all because I think my definition of the honeymoon stage is different than most. I don't mean the flowers, fancy dates, and constantly missing each other all the time. I mean that I never want to not be excited to see my husband after work. I never want to wonder if he still thinks I'm beautiful. I guess it's the complacency that I fear. I don't think I could bear the day that my husband stops looking at me when I enter a room.

To a fault, I love people so hard that I become desperate not to lose them, which is ironic because nothing puts out a flame quicker than the winds of desperation. I've never known love to be a lasting thing, but I still have a tiny seed of hope blooming in the deepest cave of my heart and every so often, at just the right angle through all the jagged and broken walls of that cave, some sunlight creeps in to nourish that tiny bloom. Like a cactus needs the rain but only sparingly, my heart needs those tiny shards of true love that I see in the world to keep my tiny bloom of hope from withering away in the wind entirely.

It did not go well, by the way, with that old flame, as you may have guessed. I was fresh out of a relationship and my panic attacks were hitting hard every time I tried to go to his house to see him. I would be okay going to Silvy's apartment or her mom's house some nights but even then, I would still have to unexpectedly go home to nurse a panic attack on occasion. It's pretty defeating trying to explain panic attacks to someone who can't even remotely relate to them and it's even more defeating to explain them to someone who doesn't care to try to understand them either.

I remember one particular evening I spent bawling my eyes out on my living room floor because I was supposed to go to this ex-flame's house, but I couldn't get myself to leave the house. The panic just wasn't having it that day and I had to find a way to describe this to him without sounding like I had been snorting meth all day and now the voices were telling me to stay inside OR ELSE.

Going anywhere at all was a big thing for me those first few months back home. I was scared I would be too far from an ER or that I wouldn't know where the closest hospital was and that would trigger a panic attack. To say the least, I didn't travel well. I still have not flown in over four years because I had one horribly turbulent flight that resulted in the child in front of me asking his Mommy if we were all going to die and me shaking my head "yes" hoping he couldn't see me. I was convinced this was where I would die, and I vowed to God that I would never fly again. I did, because I had to get back home, or I would lose my job, but I was completely knocked out on a borrowed Xanax from Silvy for the first two hours and the remaining hour was spent begging the flight attendant to slip me something to knock me back out. In my desperation, I took a pill from the woman sitting behind me that never ended up kicking in. The plane landed safely but not before I spent twenty minutes wringing my hands in a desperate attempt to clamp my jaws together, so I didn't scream "YOU HAVE TO LAND THE PLANE RIGHT NOW! I'M DYING!" Since then, I have not been able to travel to an unfamiliar place without having a panic attack. I get so scared that I won't be near an ER where they can safely knock me out to make the panic stop.

So, when I made the decision to leave my house and go to an unfamiliar place (downtown Cleveland) to watch a baseball game with this old flame, it was a huge deal for me. I had finally gotten so frustrated with missing out on all the things I so desperately wanted to do that I said to myself, "Enough is enough, we're going to an Indians game because you love the Indians, and you want to watch them play."

I loaded up my little Coach cross-body purse with handfuls of pills (Imodium to ensure that I don't have to do anything every single human does, my Klonopin for panic attacks, my beta blockers to hopefully prevent a panic attack, and melatonin in case I need to full-on knock myself out), my "worry stone", my insurance card and the lucky stone Silvy's mother had given me when she balanced my chakras earlier that week (shut up, I do yoga and get my chakras balanced, whatever). I needed all the help I could get though; I wasn't sure how this little adventure was going to go but I was determined to stop living in fear and start living my life again. This was my first small step for mankind and a giant step for living through anxiety and panic disorder or whatever Neil Armstrong said.

We hit city traffic on the way to the game and I had a moment of fear that I would have a giant panic attack right here on 480 and we would be too trapped in the sea of cars to get any help, but thankfully the traffic moved pretty quickly and I made it through. I think I was just so desperate to feel normal again that it finally outweighed my anxiety. I was scared but I was also determined to enjoy myself and have fun before I eventually forgot what that felt like. I enjoyed myself so much that I even belted out "Come on Eileen" at the top of my lungs on the way home without so much as batting an eye to the traffic blocking our exit. I finally felt free that night. The beers probably helped a little bit.

Leaving Progressive Field with a good buzz and fireworks going off behind us was one of the best feelings. I had made it through an entire baseball game without incident (unless you count not being able to find my seat when I came back from the bathroom and having to ask the attendant where my mommy was basically) and it felt amazing. This opened so many new doors for my mental health; I had proven that I didn't need to stay at home for the rest of my life just because it was super close to an ER. It proved that I could enjoy my life and I didn't have to always live my life one panic attack at a time. However, as it goes with anxiety, this feeling of overcoming your panic attacks comes and goes and cannot always be sustained. That's another thing that took me a long time to learn, there's no end all be all for anxiety because just as I am constantly changing and growing, so is my anxiety.

However, after that successful baseball game, I was blissfully convinced that I was now cured of all panic attacks. I couldn't wait to keep pushing my limits and seeing just how much life I could live before the anxiety monster found me again, so the next weekend Silvy and her mom took me to a concert at the House of Blues in Cleveland where I got to meet one of my all-time favorite musicians, Andrew McMahon. We got to go backstage to have a beer with the band and go out behind the venue to see the tour bus. I HAD A BEER WITH THE WILDERNESS, ZAC CLARK, BOB OXBLOOD, AND ALLEN STONE. I mean come on! Who do I think I even am? I would have completely missed out on this incredible opportunity had I let my anxiety keep me at home in my room. It was one of the best nights of my life, I wish I could relive it a million more times. In at least one of those relived moments, I definitely wouldn't have just stared at Andrew McMahon with my mouth hanging open like a star-crossed pre-teen. I blame all the beers for that one though, I'd like to hope that's not how I would actually go about meeting one of my idols had I been in my right mind (sorry Andrew! Can I call you Andrew? We're pals now, right?)

However, what goes up must always come down and these anxiety triumphs were no acceptance to the rule. My panic attacks quickly resumed the following week.

The best way to describe the trials and tribulations of managing panic attacks is that it's like an eternal game of whack-a-mole but with irrational fears and the mallet is a new healthy coping mechanism you have to pull out of your ass at any given moment. What's safe one day can be a trigger the next and unfortunately, this was the case for me. I had more panic attacks after that night but none that required an ER visit (thank God) now that I was at home with my wonder-woman mother who can make my entire world feel safe with just the touch of her hand.

Mr. old/new flame couldn't handle all the back and forth of my mood swings and panic attacks, so things ended. I can't say I blame him; if you can't handle something, you can't handle it and that's fine. Panic attacks aren't for the weak, my friend. Thanks for playing though. While it hurt to see him go because of something I couldn't control; I was also a bit relieved. I knew that old flame wasn't the right one for me, but I also didn't want to be the one who said that aloud.

Now that the old flame was finally extinguished for good, I felt like I was missing something bigger in my life. I just couldn't figure out what it was. I explained this to Silvy knowing that she would know what to do. Silvy and I have always done this dance where I tell her how I'm feeling and she spits out an answer to my problems like it's the most obvious thing in the world, and often it is the most obvious resolution, it's just not the one I want to hear. In typical Silvy fashion, she plopped into my outstretched hands the suggestion of downloading a dating app. I couldn't help myself as I utterly scoffed at her, appalled. *Me? God's gift to Earth? Need a dating app? Hah! Who wouldn't want a woman who pops Imodium like tic-tacs and sometimes can't leave her house for weeks at a time?* It was a complete mystery to me as to why I wasn't finding love in the little college-town of Kent, Ohio on my own. She was right though, as Silvy usually is. It was time for something new. From her giant bean-bag chair in her drab-fab apartment Silvy flashed her "I know I'm right" grin that always showcased how annoyingly effortless her beauty was as she realized she had won yet another battle.

So, that night, I begrudgingly downloaded the dating app and I'm positive that part of my pride shriveled up and died as I filled out the questionnaire and uploaded my selfies. Given that this was my first time using a dating app, I didn't know the rules. I didn't realize you were supposed to post revealing pictures, omit the pictures that involve your cats, and maybe not mention that your favorite band is Bon Jovi. My pictures mostly consisted of my smile that three years of braces had crafted into something I was happy to show off and my loose brown curls to frame it. In other words, it was a "safe" and presumably very boring profile. Everyone's gotta start with that rookie dating profile though. Live and learn.

If nothing else, I highly recommend downloading a dating app at least once in your life for entertainment purposes. Pop open a bottle of Rosé and just swipe away, the bios and corny one-liners are hilarious. However, if you want to use them to actually find love, I suggest you develop a thick skin, a phenomenal bullshit detector and a dark sense of humor - you will need them all to survive. If I told you that the very first person I ever met on a dating app was the absolute love of my life, would you believe me? Wouldn't that just be too cliche? Could you imagine?! I mean that doesn't happen right? Right? Tell me I'm right.

I received one of my first messages from a guy named Tanner and I quickly skimmed his pictures and bio. It was refreshing to see in his photos that he wasn't out at a college bar wearing a pastel t-shirt and a backwards NBA hat like most of the other prospects. I liked his tattoos, his kind eyes, and how tall he was, so I opened his message.

It honestly wasn't even a great first message. In fact, it really sucked, and I only replied to be a sarcastic asshole because I assumed he was going to be just as shady as the other fellas on that reputable app. "Hey, what're you doing tonight?" I rolled my eyes, assuming this was going to lead to something gross like "you should come over lol" I typed out "Not you" and then decided to be just a smidge nicer for the hell of it. "Just watching the Cavs suck ass" was the cunning response that I decided to go with.

He later admitted to me that he only responded to my dry remark about the Cavs because he was also watching the game and they really were sucking ass but he had never heard that term before and it made him laugh. As we chatted more,

I realized that he wasn't some douchey college guy after all. From what he had told me, he was writing a book and a couple of screen plays. Most guys my age, especially the ones on dating apps, don't write or read books, let alone go out of their way to tell girls about it just in case it comes off as "nerdy." He spoke with such intelligence and passion that within just a few messages I was completely captivated by him; I mean how often do you meet an attractive man that not only has access to his brain but also enjoys utilizing it? What's more, he's interested in you as well and asked you on a date? My alarm clock brain pinged off little "Too good to be true!" sirens and I snoozed every last one.

Had I said anything else in that reply or had I never answered it at all, who knows where I would be now. I often wonder if I would be happier or worse off, less anxious or more anxious, happily in love, dead, in another state, a college drop-out, a published author, a yoga instructor, 300 pounds, etc. It's terrifying what one message, five words, can do to completely upend your entire life.

I still don't really understand why it happened or what it was supposed to mean for my life, but I thank God and the universe every day that it did. What if the Cleveland Cavaliers hadn't been completely blowing their 2018 season and I had said "just reading" like I normally would've been doing? What would have happened then?

Before I get too far ahead of myself, let me

just tell you about the first date. All you love haters are going to HATE that chapter because it is painfully beautiful. I mean, I can't even believe it happened to me honestly. You would've fallen in love too! I will always remember this as the best date of my entire life and there are a lot of guys who are about to be really hurt by that, but I can't even apologize. Oh God it hurts my heart so much to talk about it now, but I will do it for you my beautiful and loyal readers. Okay, enough stalling, let's do this! Turn that page! (Say it like "Move that bus!")

3

I had never been as pissed off with my entire wardrobe as I was on this less-than-lovely June evening. The weather was going to be chillier than usual for an early-summer night in Northeast Ohio and of course, given that it was Northeast Ohio, there was a chance of rain. For guys, that forecast probably just means better bring a hoodie, but for girls it means you can't straighten your hair, you have to opt for your shitty waterproof mascara, and you better not wear any open-toe shoes. I was choosing between the six "nice" shirts in my closet that hadn't quite fit me in years and the two good shirts that did fit me, so my options were limited.

After sending Silvy pictures of a million and two different outfit options, panic-drinking two light beers and desperately trying to learn to curl my hair with a flat-iron, we decided on a dark pair of jeans, a stupid olive-green shirt that I never wore again after that night and my grey slip-on converse. Tanner and I were just going to the local Panini's Bar and Grill so there was no need to overdo it (that's what I told myself after I realized I didn't have any nice shoes that weren't sandals.) I added a bit more mascara than was probably necessary as I have my father's tiny bird-like eyes and with one final look in the mirror, I decided that I looked casual but not lazy; dressed up but not trying too hard. *That'll do pig, that'll do,* I thought to myself as I laughed and turned off my flat iron.

I know I probably just made a lot of women sad by inadvertently confessing that I fell in love at a Panini's while wearing tennis shoes on a first date, but just stick with me here. That's not how I would've ideally planned it either, but we live on God's time honey.

I do everything within some range of panic, so of course, meeting a stranger in person who I only started conversing with online a few days prior was *freaking* me out. I could practically hear what my mother would say to the cops when they asked her if she realized her daughter was missing because she met a stranger online. I opened my phone to cancel the date more times than I care to remember. *I'll just tell him there was a family emergency or that I ate some bad seafood the night before!* I spent most of my quick drive to downtown Kent thinking of lame excuses to get out of this date. My hands were so sweaty that the touchscreen on my phone wouldn't register the excuse I would have chosen to type out anyway.

But, just like the Indians game with Mr. Old

Flame and the concert with Silvy, this date was something I had to do for myself. I had to prove that I could be the girl who goes on blind dates without having to leave as soon as she arrives because of a self-induced panic attack in the parking lot. I just wanted to be the girl who goes on dates in general, come to think of it. I so badly wanted to be "normal" and this date with Tanner was something I knew I would regret if I didn't see it through. So, I sent Silvy my location from my phone and silently thanked myself for picking a well-lit pub as the setting for our first date. The sense of familiarity would hopefully be on my side.

I had told Tanner I was nervous about meeting a stranger and he had chuckled at my caution and proceeded to assure me that he would bring two different forms of ID if that would make me feel better. I laughed at his discretion but also thought to myself that I wouldn't be totally against this idea, joking or not. I mean, the dude didn't have any social media platforms to his name so I was already certain I was going to be grabbing a drink with someone's bald great-uncle that may or may not have a warrant out for his arrest in three different states. I have my anxiety to thank for that though, always ensuring that I am prepared for the absolute worst-case scenario.

Silvy was so excited and happy for me, a true cheerleader, that she was really the only reason I left my house and showed up for that date despite my buzzing nervous system. The potential of a panic attack was knocking around in my brain like *HEY! HEY THIS IS GOING TO BE TERRIFYING, DO NOT GET OUT OF YOUR CAR!* but something about the way Tanner had been easing my mind and accidentally convincing me to show up made me think this was not something I wanted to miss out on.

I showed up to the bar about fifteen minutes early because I HATE to be the person who awkwardly walks in last and pans across the room, examining every single face in the vicinity for the person they're here to meet. It's the vulnerability in that painfully awkward dance of internal dialogue while scanning the room like a robot: *"Oh is that him? Suddenly, I don't remember what his hair looks like in the pictures. I guess it could be him. I'll just wait until he turns around. Should I just go up to him? Oh my god, nope not him. That is a woman."*

Rather, I like to be the person who sits there confidently swilling their wine like "what a dumbass, I'm sitting right here, how do they not see me?" Maybe that doesn't really happen to normal people, but my anxious brain says it does and clearly, it knows best here.

As I took my place at the sticky wooden-top bar, I decided to continue my pattern of drinking light beer instead of mixing things up, airing on the side of caution. I ordered a very sad and very tall Blue Moon draft. The bartender served me my tall mug with an orange slice dangling from the frosted rim and then all that was left to do was wait for Tanner to show up while I pulled on my beer. I attempted to train my focus on the Indians game that was playing on the flat screen tv hanging above the bar. It was no use, I kept finding myself looking in the reflection of the screen instead of watching the players round the bases. In the dark reflection of the LED screen, I could see the front doors opening and closing behind me while patrons passed through aimlessly. I analyzed each silhouette, judging whether their shape and size potentially matched that of Tanner. I was so anxious to finally come face-to-face with the man behind the dating profile picture that I barely registered the baseball game playing on my makeshift rearview mirror.

Tanner was proving to be fashionably late, and I began playing through the self-sabotaging thoughts of *"he may never show up or"* that *"he probably had changed his mind because you scared him off."* I tried not to picture myself waiting alone at the bar for hours as a dramatic time-lapse video showed my beer glass draining incrementally.

Before I had time to shoo away those thoughts, I felt him enter the room with a *whoosh* of the heavy front doors. I didn't even have to look up to know it was him, every hair on my body stood tall at once and my stomach leaped to my throat with excitement. I saw a figure approach the bar out of the corner of my eye in a confident way that suggested he was just grabbing a drink from the bartender or maybe closing his tab. Like he had been here a thousand times and knew exactly what he wanted; no draft list necessary. I couldn't bring myself to turn my head in his direction and I couldn't figure out what exactly I was afraid to see. That my idea of the fat uncle was true? That he looked nothing like his pictures? Or maybe it wasn't him at all and it was just another regular ordering a drink and my intuitive feeling of him next to me was false? It was that achingly tantalizing feeling of *"Oh my God this is it, this is the moment you've been waiting for!"*

Holding my breath, I gathered up the courage to face him. *No turning back now.* I finally peered over, and I instantly started blushing at what I saw leaning up against the bar. Tanner, in fact, did not look like his pictures. He looked like the perfectly photoshopped, more matured version of the man in his pictures. I remember thinking "Silvy is never going to believe this" because I myself could not believe it either. You always hear the catfish horror stories but when do you ever hear "He looked even better than his pictures!" Never.

The first thing I noticed was his height - he stood at about 6'3", maybe even 6'4." I had to crane my neck up to see his eyes. He was very tanned and toned from working long hours in the sun and his dark hair was cropped short and a bit shaggy.

Wearing a modest black V-neck shirt and fitted khaki pants with black casual shoes to match, he went for the simple look just like I did - thankfully. His left arm was almost entirely covered in tattoos that I couldn't quite make out from a distance, but one appeared to be in the shape of... Ohio? A cat perhaps? God, I loved tattoos on a tall man.

He looked so innocent while he nervously fumbled around in his wallet for his ID that I almost didn't even want to speak up and tell him I was sitting right beside him. I wanted to take one more minute to be an outsider looking in on this beautiful moment before lifting the veil and taking part in it. A tall, dark and handsome, tattooed man of my actual dreams was here in this sports bar looking for *me*. The fact that a man who looked as inhumanly perfect as he did and was nervous to meet me made me want him even more. Tanner didn't even know that I was about a foot or two away from him and he had already made me feel like the only girl in the bar. And as I relished in this feeling, all I could make myself spit out to get his attention was "Hey."

When he looked over to see who had addressed him, we locked our eyes, and he unveiled a relieved smile that all but knocked the wind out of me. It was as if he was also relieved to see that I was the woman I had promised to be in my profile pictures. Maybe he had been expecting someone's bald uncle as well, but regardless, he seemed pleasantly surprised with who he saw staring back at him expectantly.

"Hey! Baleigh?" I had to bite my tongue to stop at "Yes! You must be Tanner," and not continue on to say "Yes, man that is made of all that is perfect, it is I, Baleigh. And I love you." Tanner was very smooth, so when he said, "I didn't think it was you because I thought *there's no way that girl doesn't have a boyfriend,*" I was charmed but I still playfully rolled my eyes. Whether he meant it or not, I was desperate to remain wary because all that I have been taught from men and dating is that if it seems too good to be true, it probably is.

He didn't have to say anything smooth at all, he truly didn't, because the moment he slid closer to me and smiled at me like he had known me for years, I experienced that moment that everyone in all the worst cheesy movies talk about. The corny "love at first sight" moment that most rational people don't even believe in. Although, it wasn't a spark flying, naked-baby-shooting-an-arrow, foot-popping moment. It was more of an entire body realization, an "ohhhhhh okay, there it is" moment where my heart finally relaxed and allowed itself to be at home with another person's soul.

My shoulders relaxed, a genuine toothy smile melted over my entire face and my inner voice said, "We're home now, he is the person you were always meant to find."

Being that I am a person needing factual evidence, examples and testimonials to believe anything at all, I could never wrap my head around the "when you know, you know" explanation of love, but in this moment, I finally understood the saying. The dimmer-switch on my world was pushed up as high as it could go, and the sudden flash of light was blinding but I welcomed it like the sun.

When you hear about a "crooked smile" in a classic country love song, it's hard to picture one that doesn't resemble Drew Barrymore laughing at an Adam Sandler joke, but I understood that now too. Tanner's sweet smile wasn't so much crooked as it was lopsided. The right corner of his mouth pulled up toward his eye just a bit more than the other side in a natural way that no one else could ever mimic. It was a half-moon leaning up against the heaviness of millions of tiny stars. The lazy smile only further enhanced his smoldering s'mores for eyes. I use that metaphor because that is exactly what they reminded me of. The whites of his eyes were so pure that the contrast of the chocolatey brown iris reminded me of a heavy blanket wrapped around me while I smushed Hershey chocolate and a golden marshmallow between two Great Value graham crackers. His warm skin tone created the heat of the bonfire, and I swore I could even smell a hazy smoke in the distance.

When Tanner ordered an Elvis Juice, I instantly regretted my Blue Moon choice and wished

I had gone for something a little less domestic like I usually would have. Licking his first sip from his lips he grinned and nodded at my beer while muttering "Not much of an IPA girl, huh?" I sheepishly laughed and said "No, they all taste the same to me unfortunately-gross." He replied with "Well, I'm an IPA girl." as he laughed and laid easily back into his bar stool. I laughed my big unedited laugh that slips out when something funny genuinely catches me off guard and I instinctively covered my mouth to try and erase the sound from ever leaving my lips. I waited for him to say, "What in the actual hell was that?" because that's the usual response I get to my laugh. Tanner laughed and told me to put my hand down and to never apologize for a real laugh. The way he said these cliché charming little nothings didn't sound arrogant like it would be coming from any other man. He meant every word of what he said.

I lost track of how long we had been talking about our families, jobs, education, and more and my neck was starting to hurt from turning my head towards him for so long. I was absent-mindedly rubbing the kinks from my neck when Tanner flagged the host down and asked her if we could get a table where we could sit face-to-face rather than sit side-by-side at the bar. I tried not to show how impressed I was that he was watching me that intently.

Once we were seated at a high-top, I told

him all my juiciest life stories, like how my half-sister had found me on the internet and how I drove to Georgia to meet her and my other sister. I told him about the time I cut my foot open in the Cuyahoga River and someone's dog led me to his owner who just so happened to know my grand-parents and ended up giving me a ride to the ER. He ate up every single detail like I was preaching the word of God. He stared so intently into my eyes while I spoke that it was borderline unnerving. I touched briefly on my struggles with anxiety and panic attacks, but I wasn't ready to disclose the se-verity of my disorder yet. I wanted him to believe I was "normal", like him, for as long as possible.

His eyes pierced through me with the fervor of a child's while watching their favorite part of a beloved Pixar movie, with unwavering attention and unshakeable eye contact. It was foreign to me, to truly be heard, but I grew to adore it; to crave it even as the night went on.

Tanner says things impulsively, without a buffer, so when he blurted out during a pause in conversation that my eyes were strikingly beau-tiful it caught me so off-guard, I almost couldn't reply. I blushed as I thanked him. "Of course!" he said, "I'm sorry, I just noticed how many different colors were in them. Unlike any I've ever seen be-fore," as he leaned in ever so slightly closer to me. My skin was on fire seeing how close his face was to my own now. He was remarkably beautiful; I was transfixed immediately.

Tanner told his own life stories with just as much intensity as he displayed while listening to mine. He told me of how he hitchhiked to South Carolina on a whim in his early twenties and how he hiked through the mountains of Utah and came across a moose that captivated him by its grace. At one point, he became so animated while regaling me with another travel story that he got out of his chair and was standing in the aisle reenacting a moment where he was dangerously straddling something in his story with both hands clutching invisible railings. It was like he couldn't even see anyone else in the bar, let alone care if they were judging or watching him. I, on the other hand, couldn't help but look around the bar to see if people were looking at him. And they were. At the time, I was so embarrassed by this. I'm ashamed now that I even cared about what everyone else was thinking of him at that moment.

Tanner was being fully himself, and vulnerable albeit to a fault, but all I could think about was what those other people were saying to each other about him. I missed entirely what he had been talking about and that story was erased from my memory forever now. It looked like it was a good one too. Tanner, whether he noticed or not, didn't care at all who was watching. His eyes were on me, and to him, it was just the two of us in that bar. I envied him for his self-confidence.

I wanted to learn everything about this man, I could've sat there all night taking in anything he was willing to share with me. The conversation began with him asking me to tell him about myself and flowed into me, sharing every detail I had. I remember coyly asking what he wanted to know, and he matched my coyness with "Anything. I want to hear anything you'll tell me about yourself," as if he had read my mind. So, I did just as he had asked.

I learned a lot about Tanner that night too of course, like, his favorite band was Def Leppard while mine was Bon Jovi. I found this to be completely endearing because I had gotten so much hate growing up for loving a corny 80's band while most kids my age were swooning over Fall Out Boy and the Biebs. Tanner had also spent some time at Hilton Head Island, which I easily related to because of the time I had spent living just a couple hours north in Wilmington. He was very close with his mother, as was I and I loved that too. There is nothing more important to me than my mother and it warmed my soul to know he fully agreed. This was also the night that I learned if you asked Tanner where he felt the most at home, he would tell you "In the water." It didn't matter if it was a stream, the Cuyahoga River or the Pacific Ocean, he loved it all and could spend hours floating, swimming, and diving beneath the waves. I nodded my head in agreement as I too had fallen in love with the ocean that I called home for three short years.

I was in awe at how well this date was going in comparison to the train wrecks from my past. I typically went for the guys who didn't want to be seen in public with me and would rather die than enter a committed relationship. The entire world had just been placed in the cheap leather bar stool across from me and I wanted to revel in that for as long as I could, so I sipped my beer a little slower. I sensed that Tanner was thinking the same, but I couldn't bear to hear him say it aloud and break the spell. I scrambled to change the subject before he could jinx our luck by saying "wow we seem to really have a lot in common!" but the beer was beginning to cloud my judgment and I came up short.

Beer number three decided it would be best if I finally told Tanner that he had spinach in his teeth from the artichoke dip. It's amazing how far I will go to stop a man from enjoying my company. Thankfully, he was very grateful for my honesty and slipped off to the men's room to assess the damage. This gave me time to check my phone and text Silvy that not only was Tanner not some-body's creepy uncle but that I was, and I quote, "in love, in love, and I don't care who knows it!" with a GIF of Buddy the Elf spinning around in his father's Empire State Building office. She was incredibly relieved and excited for me as she exclaimed "Great!!! You deserve it! But still be careful, you don't know him that well yet. Love you, have fun!" I quickly assured her she would still have my location indefinitely as Tanner emerged from the bathroom and walked back to our table.

As he made his way back to me, I thought to myself that I still couldn't believe this night was happening and that he was enjoying it just as much as I was. I could hardly contain my excitement and anticipation of what the world had in store for us next.

Tanner and I continued to talk for a few more hours. The sun had set, and the moon was looming high above the trees. We shared an appetizer and two more beers. Later, I would lie in bed and calculate that we had talked for four hours in the bar that night. I didn't even know I had that much to say, nor the attention span to listen to someone else speak for that long, but time slipped by like water.

When he asked, "Would you like to go play billiards?" I accidentally laughed right in his beautiful face. Part of this accidental laugh was because I couldn't believe he called it "billiards" like he was Colonel Mustard, and the other part was out of shock that he wanted to keep this night going as much as I did. I was nervous because you know anyone that calls pool "billiards" is good at it, but I was floating on a Blue Moon cloud, so I was up for the challenge. He paid the tab while I freshened up in the bathroom and we walked a block down the street to a hole-in-the-wall bar that had four pool tables and thankfully not too many people. We both preferred the lame bars to the overcrowded ones across the street, so we settled right into our new corner table.

We saddled up to the bar and Tanner ordered a beer while I scoped out the cave-like environment of the dive bar. Given that Tanner was a self-proclaimed IPA girl, I wasn't surprised when he ordered a Mystic Mama that came in a trendy black and purple can. I impishly ordered a Bud Light because the beers from the previous spot were starting to hit me all at once and I knew I had to drive home (and everyone knows that Bud Light is actually just water, duh). We set our beers at the table and Tanner racked up the balls on the shabby pool table.

I warned him multiple times that I don't play "billiards", so I am a terrible shot. With his crooked smile, he assured me that he would go easy on me until I started showing signs that I was just out to hustle him. Tanner tried with all he had to give me some pointers and help me with my technique, but I was helpless. At one point I made a shot that never even managed to hit a single ball on the table; my stick just shot straight up in the air, and I hung my head as I laughed at myself. I hoped that this horrible shot had come off as endearing and not annoying. I really wasn't trying to be this terrible at pool despite how it looked. I was afraid to look up and see if he was laughing at me but when I looked up, Tanner was laughing in a "it's okay you tried!" way that some people look at kids when they miss the baseball on the tee after a huge swing of the bat. He was then making his way over to me to help me out yet again and saying "You were so close! There was a lot of power behind that one!" he chided jokingly. I was grateful for his patience and his genuine need to ensure that I left a better "billiards" player than when I had arrived. Even if it was to no avail.

Eventually an older couple approached the table and asked if we wanted to play on teams and I watched in horror as Tanner happily replied "of course!" The couple was friendly, and my second "water" was starting to kick in, so we dove into a spirited round of "billiards" to which we humbly lost. As we were high fiving our new friends, the fit began to hit the shan.

At about midnight the bartender had come to our tables and began collecting our beers (beers we were still drinking) and putting the pool sticks away. The older man and woman began to protest and ask the woman what the hell she was doing to which she haughtily replied, "We're closing early, my sitter can't stay any longer." It was a weekend night in downtown Kent and there were a good amount of people still milling around the bar but before we could even mention this fact, the nasty waitress scoffed "If you have a problem with it take it up with the manager because I don't give a shit." As it would happen, both Tanner and the couple we had been playing pool against really did know the owner and they assured her they would be letting him know.

Defeatedly, the older couple, Tanner and I gathered our things, paid our tab and headed towards the door. Tanner and I were both in shock by the way that woman had just spoken to us, but this is the thing about Tanner; he sees everything as an opportunity to make a memory or a positive impact. As fate would have it, three drunken college guys were trying to head into the bar as we were walking out, and they asked us if the bar was still open. Without missing a beat Tanner replied "Yes they are! They're even staying open late tonight so tell all your friends to come down! Ask for Brandy, she's the bartender and she's in a great mood tonight. She'll probably even buy you guys a round!" I just stared at Tanner in awe as the guys all proceeded to high five and called their friends from other bars to come down to the bar.

Tanner and I giggled hysterically while we walked down the street. Those poor guys had no idea what they were in for. I've always wondered what happened once they got inside the bar. As our laughter finally subsided, I became incredibly aware that Tanner was walking with his hand on the small of my back and keeping himself between the street traffic and myself. I noticed chivalry was a second language to him; never a door left unopened for me to pass through, or a tab left open for me to pay.

Between Tanner's secret smile and the warmth from his hand on my back, I felt like I was going to explode. My body hummed under the weight of his hand. At that moment, a wall of dread hit me as I realized with horror that the night was more than likely over now. I never wanted him to move his hand from my body and I wondered how soon he would want to see me again, if at all.

We reached the end of the street, and I dismally began to turn the corner towards the parking lot when Tanner stopped me and said "The night doesn't have to be over just yet, you know? I'm really enjoying my time with you tonight. Would you like to go for a walk?"

Half of me melted right then and there while the other half of me thought *Ohhhh so this is the part where he kills me, and no one ever finds my body.* I felt it in my blood that I could not only trust this man but follow him to the ends of the Earth without ever for a second being put in harm's way. Tanner exuded protection with his soft melty brown eyes. I felt protected and safe in his presence rather than guarded and skeptical like I would usually feel with, essentially, a total stranger.

We stopped at Tanner's car so he could grab a hoodie in case either of us got cold on our walk. There was a bridge that overlooked the Cuyahoga just one block over that led to a quaint little wooden gazebo. Once inside the gazebo, there was a well-lit wooden staircase that led down to the river on a hike and bike trail. I was apprehensive to go further, but I was too excited to see what lay beyond the steps to listen to my nervous brain. We approached the large cement tunnel underneath the bridge when I noticed that the light was flickering against the spray-painted walls. I couldn't help myself as I blurted out "This must be the part where you kill me, huh? It looks like we're in the movie *It*." Thankfully he understood my humor and laughed with me as he replied with "Well now the element of surprise is shot, you ruined it."

We passed through the creepy tunnel and when we emerged on the other side, I was shocked by the beauty of this trail. The street lanterns that lined the path shed an illuminating glow on the cobbled path. You could see the river rushing just below and the thick trees created an enchanted feeling of walking through a folklore forest. I had been living in Kent on and off for 11 years and could not believe I had never seen this trail. It was beautiful.

Kent was an adorable little college town right along the Cuyahoga River that was surrounded by quaint coffee shops, college bars, and a spattering of breweries and wine shops, but I never bothered to look beyond that. I had spent time walking the trails at a park not far from here that was also parallel to the rushing river bends of the Cuyahoga, but this trail put that tiny park to shame as it had to be three times larger with twice as much to look at with all the winding paths and bridges. Tanner seemed to know this trail quite well and this only added to his desirability for me.

We meandered further down the path and as we rounded a corner Tanner said, "There's a vine swing just up this hill if you'd like to sit there for a bit."

I smiled excitedly in response and nodded like a child at the thought of going on a big swing in the woods. Sure enough, there was a giant old vine hanging from a tree that looked like it had been there since the town was established and I thought *There's no way this can bear the weight of anything larger than a squirrel.* As if to read my mind, Tanner demonstrated the swing by settling into the crook of the vine's elbow and kicked his feet back and forth as he swung like a pendulum. It was obvious by how low the make-shift swing sat to the ground that only one person would fit on the swing at a time, so Tanner offered me his hand as he helped me up the hill and onto the swing to take his place. He moved so easily and with such confidence that I could tell he had spent a great deal of his life coming to this swing. With each step he took, his feet easily found the smooth patches of concrete and dodged the random root protruding from the path. Tanner was observing my reaction to each twist and turn like he couldn't wait to see if I loved this place as much as he clearly did. It was adorable, and I hoped my facial expressions conveyed how much I really was enjoying this new oasis he had brought me into.

When I looked out from my perch on the swing, I couldn't believe the view. From up here, I could look down on the rest of the path spanning out from either direction. Just a little farther down the hill from there, I could see the river rush below us too. There was a light breeze carrying the love songs of the peepers over the branches and between the leaves up to our faces. It was the most peaceful place I'd ever seen.

I remember breathing in the smell of the soil and the dampness of the river with my eyes closed and a smile on my face while I swayed lazily back and forth on the swing. I immediately fell in love with that haggard old swing, and I think Tanner sensed it because he took a seat at the foot of the hill as if he knew we were going to be there for a while.

Hearing the river below me and seeing the full moon reflecting off the white caps of the rapids brought me back to the nights in North Carolina when I would sit out on the beach during a full moon. It was my favorite thing in the world to do because it felt so surreal. It would be nighttime, but the entire ocean would be illuminated by the moon. It was like a dream; you could see clear down to your toes in waist-high water. Now I was brought back to that same dreamlike state with this man who wanted to be in it with me and could appreciate it as much as I did.

After a beat, I wondered if I had misread his interest in basking in the moonlight for a while, so I offered to keep walking. Tanner looked over his shoulder and up the hill towards where I was still swinging, smiled at me with his sparkling eyes and said, "No, take your time. You can stay on that swing all night if you'd like." This made me so happy that I had to bite back a giant cheesy smile in return. It touched my heart that he was enjoying how much I loved this moment, high up in the trees like a couple of slow-moving owls, hidden from the rest of the world as we watched it pass by below us. That moment was so sweet to me, like candy.

In his eyes, I could see my mirrored expression of lust and I knew he was tasting the sweetness of this moment as well. I couldn't know for sure but judging by the way his gaze bore through me adoringly, I thought maybe Tanner was clocking this moment as one he would never forget either.

Eventually the unforgiving firmness of the

vine swing began to numb me from the waist down, so we dragged ourselves from the hill and down the path back the way we came. Both of us wanted to milk this night for as long as we could so we walked even farther back in the other direction, all the while following the river downstream. The path dumped out into the parking lot of an apartment complex/yoga studio that sat just above the river and I was again met with the sad realization that our night must be over, assuming it was time to head back to the parking lot again. I should have known that Tanner had more hidden treasures up his sleeve; he placed his hand on my back as he led me across the tiny parking lot to yet another footpath. This time he explained to me that there was a ledge that overlooked the river if I'd like to sit with him there for a while so we could talk more. I said "of course" but I was thinking, *How could this night possibly get better?*

We walked underneath another well-lit bridge that was just a bit smaller than the last one when Tanner began to lead me off the path and through some trees. I stopped and panicked because I couldn't see a thing and had no idea where he was taking me. Tanner laughed as he remembered my earlier confession of being a complete klutz and said, "It's okay, take my hand, I'm not going to let you fall." The way that man looked into my soul with complete sincerity and those Labrador eyes I swear I would have followed him right off a cliff. And as we began heading down a steep decline, I was pretty sure that's exactly what I was doing.

When we emerged from the thicket, a rock wall appeared in front of me. It couldn't have been more than a foot wide and about fifteen feet high. At the bottom of the wall, the Cuyahoga rushed underneath us and down under another nearby overpass. We sat along the top of the wall and again, I was amazed by the view. It was a clear night with a full moon in the sky because and the black water beneath flicked and reflected beams of light back up at us like tiny camera flashes. I could smell the salty sweet scent of love on the horizon, and I wondered if it was coming from me alone or if he was the sweet and I was the salty. *Were we creating this love story together? Or was it just me?*

My anxiety had long disappeared and was now replaced with a blind adoration for this beautiful human that had been placed in my cupped hands as sweet and substantial as an old locket. I hadn't felt this at ease in so long and there wasn't a drug in the world that any doctor could prescribe me that could hold a candle to this new feeling of belonging I was experiencing on this ledge with Tanner. The warm breeze had followed us from the swing down to this rocky ledge and with its long, elegant fingers, it played with all the leaves on the trees that surrounded us. The sound of the river running below and the heat radiating off the man that sat just inches away from me was enough to soothe anyone's soul; I felt like I was truly at home.

For a beautiful moment we both just sat there, mesmerized by the beauty and the power of the rapids thumping just beneath our dangling feet, taking it all in. Tanner scooted towards me, and his calloused hand covered mine. He looked over at me and said, "I hope that's okay, you don't mind, do you?"

He was very endearing like that, a perfect gentleman. A knowing smile spilled over my face as I said I didn't mind it at all. I couldn't believe this was happening to me, up until this moment, the coolest thing that had ever happened to me was getting to meet some of the cast members from *Degrassi* at the Randolph Fair when I was 14. It felt like this was the moment I had been waiting for my entire life; the good parts of life that everyone always promised you were yet to come.

The moonlight began to dim and as I looked to the sky, a thick raindrop flicked my nose. Within seconds a soft drizzle began, just enough rain to be annoying but not quite enough to send you running for cover. Tanner put his neon-yellow work hoodie around me as I attempted to cover my hair and I was welcomed into a cloud of his scent that I can only describe as "Tanner smell." It was sweet, with a musky undertone and a hint of laundry detergent. I've never smelled anything quite like it since then. I've always found it to be so unfair that the smell of someone's belongings fade and take on the shape and form of their new surroundings like scent-chameleons.

We basked in the soft drizzle and talked about our lives and experiences as one o'clock slipped past, then two o-clock eased into three in the morning. Tanner turned to me with his half-moon smile and apologetically sighed "I suppose we should get going now." He helped me to my feet and back across the narrow wall where we ascended the now slippery ravine. His hand reached back for mine without a second thought. Whether it was so I wouldn't slip or just because he liked the way our hands seemed to find each other naturally as much as I did, I didn't know. And I didn't care.

As we walked back to our cars, a sadness creeped over the both of us that caused us to finally go quiet. The streets were empty now, and the rain had begun to pick up as we hurried over the sidewalks. Tanner took me in his arms as we waited for one lonely car to ease past us at the crosswalk. His eyes were far away when I looked up at them from where my head was resting on his chest. It was almost as if he didn't realize he was pulling me in, it just happened naturally, like putting on his seatbelt as soon as he sat in his jeep or dropping his eyes when he was nervous.

It wasn't long before we had reached the parking lot and I was leaning against my car holding my breath as I waited to hear Tanner say what was going to happen next. I leaned in to give him his hoodie back, but he stepped away and laughed as he said "No, no," then more seriously but still with a smirk, "Keep it. That way you'll have to see me again." I let out a breath I was barely aware I had been holding in. He wanted to see me again too. At that, I smiled and said that sounded perfect to me and waited for him to kiss me goodnight. However, as soon as I saw him sheepishly duck his head and flick his eyes to the shiny pavement, I knew tonight wouldn't be the night he kissed me. He was so nervous, and I ate it up. I got into my car with promises of a text upon my safe arrival home and a smile that made my face ache for weeks to come.

4

The missing part of that night was but a fleeting after-thought to me at the time. I had so much hope for my future with Tanner that the rare shortcomings dissolved from my memory almost instantly. I left this part out because I wanted you all to remember our first night together the same way I do now; with nothing staining the pure white veil of romance.

After the beautifully silent moment that Tanner and I spent together just embracing the light of the full moon on the rock wall, I asked him if he liked his job. It seemed like such a mundane question to ask after a moment like the one we had just come out of, but I had an anxious urge to fill the silence eventually. I swore I saw a shadow fall over Tanner's face before he even answered. He took a minute to come back to the present moment and reply to the question I had just imposed.

"I've been working for the hardscaping company with my father since I was 15. It's been a great job and it has served its purpose, but I need more. I want to help people and I want to do something more meaningful with my limited time on this Earth."

As I sat with the kindness and purity of that statement, I almost missed what Tanner said next:

"So, I'm planning on joining the Army. I would even like to be a Ranger someday and help those who are injured out on the field and give them the hope that they need in that vulnerable moment."

I felt the dreamworld that Tanner had spent the entire night stringing around me slowly begin to fall away then. All at once I felt hurt, stupid and incredibly helpless. Nothing was set in stone, these were just dreams that Tanner had been sharing with me, but I couldn't help but think *Of course he's leaving Baleigh, you idiot. Everyone leaves you.*

I had a hard time focusing on anything Tanner said after that, I was too busy picking apart, down to the bone, the weight of what Tanner had just shared with me. I was silently begging God to change his mind; even bargaining with him just so I could keep him here with me a little longer. While it wasn't a certain plan for Tanner yet, I already knew it was going to happen. The other shoe had dropped without me there to hear the laces whistle past my head, and I was already picturing my tearful goodbye to Tanner. You can't bargain with God though unfortunately, that's not how that works, and I knew that, but I was desperate. I wasn't ready to throw this one back to the river just yet.

I realized it was my turn to respond to what Tanner had just told me and my response immediately made me cringe. It came from a place of fear but nonetheless, I heard myself say "But you're too smart to waste your life in the military. That would be such a waste of your true potential."

Back then, after dating a marine for five years, the military was an ugly, tainted thing in my mind. It was where teenage boys threw their dreams away and dimmed their intelligence at the expense of learning to die for their country. It was a place where you wanted nothing more than to escape as soon as you entered through the stinky gates of Parris Island. With a furrowed brow and a rushed explanation, I tried to make Tanner see this.

Tanner, being the patient and understanding soul that he was, explained, "Not every branch is like the Marine Corps Baleigh, and not everyone's experience in the military is the same. Some of the most intelligent men in the world were Army Rangers or Navy SEALS."

I heard what he was saying to me, but I was not convinced. Tanner's mind was something utterly extraordinary and I was so sad to think that it would be dulled by the monotony and restraint of the military. He went on to explain that the military would also take care of his student loan debt and that he may not even get in because of his mishaps as a college kid. I understood that; I had my own underage drinking charge lingering on my record from when I was a teenager. So, I clung to that selfish shred of hope, and his hoodie, until I finally welcomed sleep with a small smile on my face that night. I was scared to lose Tanner, but I was smart enough not to let my fear ruin the best night of my life, so I left the sad part out and held the rest close to me as I slept.

When I woke up the next morning still wrapped in his hoodie, the military talk was all but wiped clear from my memory. That was the power of his scent in my sheets, and for days I was drawn to that scent like a drug because of the sense of belonging and safety it brought me. The smell of his cologne, the rain, and river breeze all entwined with the fabric of that neon yellow hoodie was all it took to make the rest of the world fade away. It was better than any anti-anxiety drug I had ever been prescribed over the years. I've tried every essential oil mixture, candle, lotion and laundry detergent since then but the scent of a person who inevitably holds your heart in their hands cannot be synthetically recreated. As I lay immersed in the warmth of that healing scent the next morning, it took all I had to leave my bed and go back to my reality. I wasn't ready to wake up from my dream yet, but my alarm clock had other plans, as it always does.

I called Silvy the next day to tell her all about my date and when she asked about what he does for a living, my heart sank as I remembered Tanner's plans to join the military. Poor Silvy tried to encourage me by saying there was no way Ranger School would ever accept him with a past record. I loved her so much for saying that, as selfish as that was, whether she truly believed it or not, she knew that I needed to hear it at that moment. In any scenario, I couldn't possibly see the military turning down a mind like Tanner's, no matter what his past held. They would eat him alive the second they heard him speak, I was sure of it. You see, when Tanner spoke about things that he was passionate about, it was like he almost went somewhere else in his mind, and he wasn't even speaking to you anymore. He would just stare off in the distance and speak directly from his heart with such fervor that you couldn't look away from him as he spoke. That was how he spoke about the military, which was also how I knew Tanner would eventually have to be someone I said goodbye to. He would never belong to me but instead to the iron grasp of the military. It hurt too much to think about, so I didn't. I pushed that thought as far away from the front of my brain as I could manage with Silvy's help.

The days following that night felt like a dream. I am consciously aware they happened but all I can remember from that time is the hazy edges of hot days spent in the shop at work counting down the minutes until Tanner's name popped up on my phone again. I was interning for a large landscaping company as a "business analyst" while I was in college in hopes of getting my foot in the door at their McMansion of a corporate office. The long July days in that shop with no air conditioning passed by slower than any other time in my entire life. I remember feeling like my body was going to sweat and sag until it eventually melted down to nothing and slipped into the drains that lined the cement garages. The texts from Tanner were few and far between since he worked a hands-on position for the hardscaping company during the days and often, well into the evenings.

We chatted for a few days and finally, a second date was set. It was all I could do not to show up three days early and wait for him by the river until then. Our river, as I began to call it.

Our "date", if you want to call it that, was set for a Friday night and Silvy and I were leaving early the next morning for New York to visit our good friend Kass. I didn't have much time between work and getting back to Silvy's to spend walking the trail with Tanner that day because of this. I regretfully explained this to Tanner and, of course, his perfect response was:

"That's okay. I would be happy even with ten minutes of your time."

He melted my heart with little messages like this sometimes. I genuinely didn't know men like him still existed, or ever existed at all for that matter. I was a 24-year-old woman, but I swear I aged backwards a year with every word he said to me until eventually I was a gushing teenager again.

Friday arrived and my workday finally ended with the halting screech of the foghorn that signaled the end of the day. I flew out of the shop as fast as I could to get a jump start on getting ready for my walk with Tanner. I was inebriated with the anticipation of seeing him again even though it was a million degrees outside, and I knew I was going to sweat right through whatever I decided to wear. I went with leggings, a tank top, black flip flops and my heart chakra bracelet from Silvy's mom for good luck. I was more confident in my appearance this time around because I lived in leggings and knew they would flatter my good curves and flatten my good-but-not-as-good-as-the-other-curves curves. With a final look in the mirror, I kissed my cats goodbye and hurried out to the car with a little extra hop in my step. Was I floating? I think I was floating. How embarrassing.

Tanner was waiting for me down by the river by the time I finally reached the Panini's parking lot, so I was hurrying across the huge bridge to get to him. While taking in the incredible view of the train tracks, the river and the valley below me, I noticed a text from Tanner that read, "Call me when you're halfway across the bridge." I thought that surely had to be a typo, but I had already reached the middle of the bridge by the time I read his text. Confused and stopping in my tracks, I dialed Tanner's number.

He answered on the second ring and asked if I was standing in the middle of the bridge, and I answered him that, yes, I was. I felt a sudden wave of self-consciousness as I realized he could probably see me from wherever he was perched, so I stood up a little straighter and subconsciously sucked in. I hated the feeling of knowing someone could see me when I couldn't see them. It was utterly unnerving, but I knew Tanner wasn't judging my looks from wherever he was hiding. His words from the other end of the line shook me from this thought as he said into my ear "Good, now look out onto the river, down past the path and over to the sandbar on the right." I looked directly underneath me, thinking he would be sitting down by the gazebo. "No," he said "Further out. Do you see me waving? You should be able to see me from that part of the bridge." I looked out towards the horizon and sure enough I saw a little speck of a man waving at me from the middle of the river. From there, it looked like he was standing on top of the water, by the way the sandbar kept him at bay. "Oh! I see you!" I exclaimed as my eyes finally found him and I waved back.

"This is where I'm going to take you to

today," he said playfully, as he faded out of sight. "I'll meet you halfway, along the boardwalk." Then the line went silent. This man always had something up his sleeve for me. I adored it.

I loved that he couldn't wait to share his favorite places with me. It showed me more about him than any gift or compliment ever could. I walked down the remainder of the bridge, through the gazebo, and out onto the boardwalk (as cool and steady as I possibly could, just in case Tanner could still see me) until I finally saw his figure approaching me from the opposite direction. Tanner was also wearing shorts and a tank top, but his shoes were MUCH different than mine. You know those toe shoes that runners sometimes wear? They look like reptilian toe socks. That's what Tanner was wearing, and I would soon learn that they were as much a part of him as his eyes and nose, as he rarely wore any other shoes if he didn't have to. He loved to be barefoot (as did I, so I understood the appeal), so those shoes were the closest he could get to a constant state of bare feet and Tanner could care less about how silly he may look in them. I poked fun at him for them all the time, but they were so endearing I hoped it never sank in.

Tanner had his hands in his pockets and was doing that awkward thing again where he nervously looked away and ducked his head rather than meet my eyes. I loved it when he did that. It was intoxicating to think I could make a man as beautiful and intelligent as Tanner feel nervous.

Our paths finally came to a head as they melted into one, and we briefly hugged each other in greeting, afraid to linger too long in the harsh light of day. I could hardly keep my feet on the ground; I wanted to jump into his arms and wrap around him like a spider monkey. *Be cool Baleigh, keep both feet on the ground,* I reprimanded myself as I forced my feet further into the wooden planks of the boardwalk below me.

We were headed off down the path not long after that and Tanner led me down another steep ravine that headed out to the river. Once we reached the sandbar, I quickly realized flip flops were no match for the rushing river currents. We walked, or stumbled I should say, out to the sandbar through the current and it took all I had to keep my shoes on my feet. The trek was worth it though because the sandbar was so peaceful and beautiful. It was like its own little island lingering smack dab in the middle of the river. Tanner told me this was one of his favorite places to read and write, and that was all I needed to hear to fall in love with it. We sat on the sandbar and talked about work and my upcoming trip to New York for a while. It was awkward because we both knew I didn't have much time and we were trying to dance around that instead of taking the time to enjoy the moment.

After about a half hour or so of wandering

around the river, we started the climb back up to the paved path. It dawned on me then why Tanner was acting so shy and nervous; after our first date, I sent him a text on the way home that said, "You forgot to kiss me!", to which he replied, "I didn't forget! I was too nervous! I couldn't do it!" Now, this being our second date, I think he felt like he *had* to kiss me. Of course, I had been joking but being that Tanner was more sensitive than most men, he was probably going crazy thinking that he had to kiss me now. I found this funny in a cruel way because finally, this was something I didn't have to worry about. I had placed the ball carefully in his court while I was just along for the ride.

The walk back to my car was quieter than it would have normally been, and I couldn't help but find it endearing that he was so nervous to kiss me. I mean come on - he was 26! We were acting like kids. I suppose I was a bit nervous too, but I was excited more than anything. It was all I had thought about since our first date together.

When we finally reached my car, we both leaned against the dusty Sonata as we finished up our conversation. Tanner stared at me with his piercing gaze that sometimes felt so raw that I felt like I was naked or growing a second head. He was staring into my eyes like he was trying to see where they ended when he said "Your eyes really are just so unique. I've never seen anything like them, it's like they're on fire." with such sincerity that it caught me off guard, yet again. That was the best compliment I had ever received, and it made me blush instantly. I thanked him and then, because I am the painfully blunt human being that I am, I uttered "You're stalling so hard" and we both burst into a fit of awkward laughter.

"I know, I know! I'm just so nervous, I'm sorry!" Tanner exclaimed as he paced back and forth through the parking lot. I stood there and giggled as he worked up the nerve to kiss me. He reached the end of the small parking lot and I heard him exhale loudly and say "Okay, okay," and he turned on his heel and rushed back towards me. In a matter of seconds, he was holding my face between his rough hands as he kissed me as softly and purposefully as I had ever been kissed.

I was grateful he was holding my face firmly in his hands because I was lightheaded at his touch and was afraid that I may be swaying back and forth. I'm no stranger to kissing, but Tanner was all new. His mouth molded to mine like memory foam; like he had been doing it for years. I could only imagine that from a distance it looked like two spare puzzle pieces fitting together with the softest *click*. I had never been kissed so carefully in my life nor had I ever felt something become part of me as seamlessly as Tanner did. In that moment, I knew where I wanted to spend the rest of my life. I knew where I was meant to be, and I thanked every God, universe, ancestor and higher power I could think of for making sure I got there right on time. I understand why I had to spend those long days in the hospital, on therapists' couches, and in cold waiting rooms. I was finally grateful for them for leading me here, to Kent, Ohio, and to this Panini's parking lot with my cheeks pressed between Tanner's hands as his smile became one with my own.

When we both finally pulled away, Tanner's drunken smile was reflected by my own wide grin that must have taken up my entire face. *He felt it too then* I thought. *Good.*

We said our goodbyes with promises to see each other again as soon as I got back from New York. I barely made it into the driver's seat without whipping out my phone to call Silvy and tell her everything that had just happened. She could tell this was the happiest I had ever been, and it made my heart feel so full to feel how happy that made her too. After my breakup with the marine, I never felt like I deserved to be loved again and assumed then that it would never happen to me again. Things had ended so horribly, and it was largely my fault. I was the villain in that story and villains spend their lives paying for their cruel deeds, so I accepted solitude as my fate. Think about it; How often do you hear of Ursella or Cruella DeVille eventually finding the love of their lives and riding off into the sunset?

Now, with Tanner, I had hope for love and

my ability to find it again. It was so close that I was afraid that if I reached out for it, it would disappear like a fragile bubble that pops in the change of the wind. Rather than jumping ahead of myself, I did something that I hadn't done in years; I indulged in my happiness and allowed myself to fully enjoy and feel it through every cell in my body. I relived the moment over ten times more in my mind, smiling a warm and teary-eyed smile all the while remembering the way his lips tasted. I listened to "Butterflies" by Kacey Musgraves on repeat the whole drive to Silvy's and finally felt like I was ready to receive a love that Ms. Musgraves would write a song about. I allowed the feeling of being adored to reintroduce itself to my vocabulary of feelings long lost and it warmed the bare skin of my cheeks like the sun. It was a euphoric feeling that I will never forget, one of the happiest days of my life.

❋ ❋ ❋

After that day, there weren't many moments with Tanner that weren't spent kissing each other. Rediscovering the value of a kiss is an amazing thing. As you grow older, it becomes something you take advantage of because it happens so often and becomes a precursor to more personal touches. When was the last time you kissed someone just to feel their mouth on yours and not because you were on your way out the door or initiating sex? Next time you kiss the person you love, be nowhere else but in that moment. Memorize the shape of their lips, the taste of their smile, the heat of their breath colliding with yours the millisecond before your lips meet. Be a teenager again and expect nothing more than a single kiss. Spend your whole day looking forward to that kiss; even let it excite you. Never let go of that feeling or become complacent, a kiss is an incredible thing. Let it be that.

5

I couldn't wait to get back to Tanner so we could pick up where we left off, leaning up against my car. When I arrived home from New York, the two of us met up by the river again to talk about my trip. I told Tanner there was a good chance it was going to rain that afternoon, but he reminded me that he loved the water, in all its forms. It was such an innocent Tanner answer that I smiled and went along with it. I drove down to my usual parking spot and joined Tanner along the path where he was waiting for me.

We talked about my trip, the panic attack I had while I was there, and how Silvy got me through it. Tanner had mentioned a few times that he wasn't afraid to die and that scared me to my core, ironically. My panic attacks had always revolved around death in some way or another, so it seemed like an impossible act, to look death in the eye with nothing but acceptance in your heart. Not for Tanner though, being the enigma that he is. He accepted that when it's time to go, that's out of his control, so why would he live in fear in the meantime? He was truly a beautiful person inside and out and I admired his confidence in the way he saw the world. We talked all about my fears, where they stemmed from, and how I dealt with them until the sun faded yet again. The sun sets so much faster out here than in the real world.

Tanner never let go of my hand when we walked the path and I loved him for that. I have always had the sweatiest hands (just blessed I guess) but he held them for hours without complaint. We always had to be touching each other. Even when we weren't paying attention or one of us (usually Tanner) was completely absorbed in another hand-flailing story, our hands would find one another in their own time. Tanner began to feel like another part of my body that moved in sync with all my other moving parts seamlessly. It was like he had always been a part of me, I just never accessed that part of myself until now. I felt like I was finally using the entirety of my body and my heart when he was near me. Before Tanner, there was so much of my imagination that had yet to be tapped into. I had never taken the time to see the world and this life to be as precious and meaningful as Tanner did. To him, all things were connected, and fear was obsolete. Whereas I took most trivial things for granted and feared something in everything. Tanner's juvenile adoration for the universe, everything that made it spin, and everything that spins inside of it was the purest form of trust I had ever witnessed. I yearned to feel as comfortable in the world as he did, all caution thrown to the wind and charging forward full speed ahead into his dreams. Drawn to him like the sun, my body a flower, I felt myself begin to bloom in his presence.

We had barely made it back up the path when it began to downpour-called it. We got to the shit bridge, (appropriately named given that it ran parallel to a pungent water-treatment plant) where we dodged between raindrops underneath the canopy of the pine trees, stopping every so often to kiss each other again, like kids. It even became a game after a while: Duck under the branches, kiss until our faces hurt or a stray jogger approached us, hurry through the rain to the next underpass of branches, repeat. Standing underneath the trees that gave minimal coverage from the rain, with Tanner's body squeezed tightly against mine to shield me from the gusty rain, I kissed him like I would die tomorrow. We were soaked and his bear-paw-like hands gently held my face up to meet his while the summer heat evaporated the ethereal mist that surrounded us. The muggy rain rose from the river and created a dreamy background for our giggling make out sessions under the trees. I looked into his chocolatey eyes and said, "Suddenly I don't mind the rain so much anymore either," just to hear his laugh as he ducked further down to laugh against my lips. *Just to see you smile, I'd do anything.*

It was always dark by the time we would leave the river on these walks because we would get lost talking about the Joe Rogan podcast (Tanner), being attacked by a beaver once and never trusting a dam again (also Tanner), and "Wildflower" being the best Bon Jovi song ever written (me, obvi). Tanner even liked that song, and he was steadfast on not liking Bon Jovi because "no one likes Bon Jovi." I'm convinced that he only ever said that to get a rise out of me, but I digress. How does a Def Leppard fan not like Bon Jovi? I was onto him.

With peepers peeping and mosquitos nipping at our arms, Tanner and I finally made it back to our cars that were fast asleep in the empty parking lot now. Saying goodbye was always the best/worst part of our river walks because that would be the kiss of all kisses, but also the last one for 4-5 days at a time because of our work schedules. We hugged our last goodbyes and trotted off to our cars for the lonely drive home. I would always sit in the driver's seat for a minute or so to come down from all the dopamine, adrenaline, and serotonin ping-ponging around my brain before driving home after my walks with Tanner. Sometimes Tanner would wait, other times he would leave me be. He never asked why it always took me so long to head home after our walks; I wonder what he thought I was doing.

After a few more of our long river walks just

like this one, I decided maybe it was time to tell my mom about Tanner...and maybe have him meet my cousin Jenna who was staying with us for the summer on the weekends. I felt like things were getting serious enough between Tanner and I that I could tell them about him without immediately regretting it. I rarely told my mom about my romantic life because things change so quickly that it almost wasn't even worth getting her excited about a new boy in her only daughter's life for no reason. I was so confident that Tanner was going to be a constant in my life that I trusted this gut feeling, however. I was terrified to talk about a man to my mother or introduce him to family because that's typically when they flee the scene. It's the kiss of death, everybody knows that! Tanner was different though; he was all I'd ever wanted.

I finally decided I would have Jenna meet him first and then if that went well, I would tell my mom about him. Jenna is the bluntest person I've ever known so I knew I could trust her for an honest analysis of Tanner, even if it was a little harsh. Jenna and I had been wanting to see the new *Jurassic World* movie, so I invited Tanner to come along with us thinking there was no way he would even be interested in meeting my family yet. I was nonchalantly trying to swallow the vomit I felt creeping up my throat when his reply popped up on my screen, almost too quickly: "Sure, sounds like fun to me! What time?" and I all but blacked out from the brick wall of anxiety that slammed into me. I guess Tanner was meeting my family. No big deal. That's fine. Everything's fine. *Oh, dear baby Jesus what have I done?*

Everything was not fine

6

I was unwell, to say the least. I was shaking, sweating, making weird gasping noises that I tried to play off as coughs as I started chugging water. All I could think was *What if I threw up in Jenna's car and Tanner sees me covered in puke?!* Even worse: *What if I puke in the theater?* and EVEN worse: *What if I puke on Tanner?!* I was picturing every terrible panic attack scenario and not any of the realistic and fun scenarios: *What if Jenna loves him and approves immediately?* Or: *What if it goes so well that he asks me to meet his mom?* Or even BETTER yet: *What if it goes so well that he meets my mom?* It never even occurred to me that this night could go well.

After a geographically short yet mentally long car ride down the road to the theater, Jenna and I arrived at the plaza. We got there before Tanner, which was good because I had bought the tickets ahead of time to assure that we would all get seats next to each other. Jenna immediately got in the popcorn line while I stood off to the side and pretended to be too "full" from dinner for any of my favorite theater snacks. I always got nervous to see Tanner, but this was different. This wasn't just another walk along our river in our own little bubble. Now, we were welcoming my cousin into the mix without the comfort and familiarity of the river gurgling in the background. When it was just Tanner and I, I could keep him to myself without the judgement of my loved ones. I was scared to bring him to the surface of our dream world because what if he was just that? A dream? My anxiety of Tanner meeting Jenna was making me feel like a stranger in my own skin. I needed to see Tanner's face. Soon.

As if I had miraculously conjured him up, Tanner's Jeep appeared in the crowded parking lot just in the nick of time. He hopped out of his old Jeep, and I was struck with the realization that an old Jeep fit the persona he was trying to project perfectly; not too flashy, sporty enough, and yet still practical and reliable. You don't usually notice an older jeep when it drives by, but you notice Tanner when he walks into a room; his Jeep-persona wasn't fooling me.

Tanner bobbed and weaved his way through the parked cars until he was close enough to the main entrance that I could make out his features. He jogged the last few steps (he must have assumed he was late) and flung the heavy glass doors open, only to be enveloped in a cloud of chatter and melted butter. Tanner surveyed the crowd until finally landing his eyes on Jenna and I waving him over. I felt the smile break across my face before I could remind myself to not look so cheesy. It happened every time I saw Tanner, I couldn't control it. Knowing that Tanner was close electrified my heart and eased my nerves simultaneously.

Tanner was wearing a drug rug (just Google it, it's not what you're picturing, Mom), cargo shorts, and his ridiculous toe shoes. Looking at Tanner's knitted pullover, Jenna and I realized at the same time that we had committed the cardinal sin of going to a movie theater: We forgot to bring hoodies. It was mid-July so a jacket or a sweatshirt was the furthest thing from our minds in this sweltering heat; it was an easy mistake to make. Tanner ducked underneath the barriers and sidled up to us with one of his best Drew Barrymore smiles yet. After I hurried through the introductions, I accidentally got right to the point; "You wouldn't happen to be wearing another shirt under your hoodie, would you?" I jokingly blurted out. His hoodie had a slight V-neckline, and I unfortunately could see that he was not wearing anything underneath it except an impossibly toned and tanned chest - wow, are you guys hot? Oh my word, what a visual.

Tanner sheepishly looked down at his hoodie and said "No, this is it. Why?" I gave him what I assumed was probably a pathetic look after glancing down at Jenna and I's T-shirts as I explained that we had forgotten to bring jackets. I was embarrassed immediately after saying that, and I tried to take it back by saying it was a million degrees outside, and that we would be just fine. This man, this beautiful perfect man, looked at me with such genuine concern for my bare arms as he said, "Oh I have an extra in my car, let me go grab it!"

Then, looking over to Jenna he added, "Would you like one too?" My heart melted. He was back underneath the barrier and jogging back through the parking lot to his car before we even had our answers out. Jenna looked over to me with wide eyes as she said "Oh we like him! What a gentleman!" Tanner's charm had claimed yet another victim. *Welcome to the club, Jenna, it's a crazy ride, I* thought to myself.

We finally settled into our seats (they were the ones closest to the aisle because in my anxiety brain, I needed to always have easy access to an exit) and I dutifully took the spot between Jenna and Tanner as the lights began to dim. We giggled through the previews together like middle schoolers until the remaining lights dimmed entirely, and the opening scene began to grow on the screen like a fungus. The second all the lights were off, we sat in pitch black waiting for Chris Pratt to light up the screen, and I became painfully aware that if I needed to throw up, I would have to get past Tanner to get out. This is what my anxiety does - it sees me having fun and being a normal person and then it screams into my ear like a snarky bitch "BUT WHAT IF YOU THREW UP RIGHT NOW? DON'T YOU FEEL YOUR STOMACH TURNING?! YOU'RE DEFINITELY GONNA PUKE, BITCH." I hold my anxiety in my stomach because in the 5th grade, my locker partner threw up in class and I was so horrified by that scene that I decided I, personally, would never vomit again so then my body had to uphold that impossible standard forever OR ELSE. Ever since then, my panic attacks have manifested in digestive issues that you 100% do not need me to spell out in this book. Maybe the next one.

That was all I thought about for the next hour - that I was going to throw up any second now. I don't even remember feeling like I had to throw up, but my anxiety had just made it apparent that it was inevitable, so my brain went along with it. To this day, I still have no idea how the first hour of Jurassic World played out, I heard it was great.

Tanner sat next to me, his warm hand on my clammy thigh, blissfully unaware that I was silently deciding whether to puke in his lap or on his beloved shoes.

I still managed to "ooh" and "ahhh" when everyone else did, and laughed when I was expected to, but I wasn't *really* there; I was trapped in a panicked world. I had been "getting through" fun activities for so long now that I could utilize my social cues without even being mentally present; my body switched to autopilot in social settings to protect myself from getting embarrassed when someone notices I'm acting anxiously. Tanner was holding my hand now, but I had no idea how he was managing to do that; it had to be like trying to hold a frozen bar of wet soap. I'm sure I was doing a good amount of nervous-sweating and fidgeting with my fingers. I sat there for twenty minutes willing myself to just let go of his hand and excuse myself so I could go panic in the bathroom alone, like I would normally do.

It finally came down to me deciding that I was absolutely going to puke. It was going to be dramatic and the lights would come on, the movie would stop, and I would die right there on the sticky floor in a pool of my own embarrassment. So, seconds before I physically crawled out of my own skin like a shell, I finally let go of Tanner's hand and politely let him know I had to pee. In those exact words. Always such a lady.

I focused on walking at a normal-person pace until I was out of the theater. *Left foot, right foot, slower, left foot, right foot, slower, okay maybe even slower than that, SLOW DOWN* and then I bounded up the ramp to the bathroom like a feral cat. The first thing I noticed when I slipped into the bathroom was the nauseating wall-to-wall pink wallpaper and the Danny-DeVito-sized stalls. This was clearly not the place for my panic attack to happen either. I quickly peed, washed my hands, and searched the lobby area for a secluded bench to get myself together.

I found a little nook that was tucked just ahead of our theater. It had its own sitting area and was, thankfully, completely abandoned. I let go of the breath I had been holding for what seemed like hours and sagged into the bench. I put my head in my hands and stared at the old retro carpet under my feet until my eyes burned. This was an incredibly sobering moment for me; I couldn't believe I was allowing my anxiety to ruin this moment with Tanner and Jenna. It had won again. *Fuck you anxiety, just give me my life back,* I thought helplessly.

The hysteria in my brain cleared just long enough for me to see this situation from outside my own panic. I was missing out on the one thing that always made me want to scream with excitement-spending time with Tanner. And for what? To coddle my anxiety and feed my fat-cat fears of public embarrassment? It was horrifying to realize that my own brain was mutilating the happiness I had been working so hard to cultivate this summer. The defeat of realizing your brain is your own worst tormentor, not others or outside forces beyond your control, is unlike any other. I was tired of feeling helpless.

I sat on the bench for a few more cleansing

breaths as I tried, yet again, to get myself together. Finally, I realized that Jenna and Tanner were probably awkwardly sitting together wondering if I was shitting to death or if I had been kidnapped and that one of them would probably come looking for me soon. I sent a group chat to them in a desperate attempt to downplay this embarrassing situation that was most likely only mortifying in my own mind. I said something like "Don't mind me, just having a mild panic attack as usual! Finish the movie without me!" like a weirdo. Who would read that and go "Okay! Have fun! Text us when you're done!"?

I tend to do everything in my power to not scare other people with my panic attacks, ironically. I could be on the verge of jumping off a building just to escape my panic, and still worry about who would have to clean up the mess on the ground. I wondered if now this movie theater bench was my skyscraper and Tanner was the one looking up at me, ready to clean up the impending mess.

I was expecting Jenna to come out so we could call my mom and have her talk me off the edge of this metaphorical building but when I looked up, Tanner was the one walking towards me with my favorite smile plastered across his face. I scooted over so he could sit next to me and the first thing he said was "It was because you weren't sitting closest to the aisle, wasn't it?"

It was eerie how easily he could read me and knew what I was thinking long before I did. In my past experiences, explaining anxiety to a guy who doesn't have it himself is like trying to explain tampon insertion to men. It's horrifying and embarrassing for both parties and the guy doesn't really want to know how it works in the first place. He just wants the conversation to stop.

I was so grateful not to have to explain my irrational fears out loud to Tanner that my body melted with relief against his shoulder.

"Why didn't you just ask me to switch seats, you dork?" he asked playfully. Hearing him say it made it sound so easy. Probably because it really would have just been that easy, but my anxiety liked to take the simplest tasks and mold them into something insurmountable for me. I laughed and said, "I know, I know."

Tanner and I sat on that bench for a half an hour while he rubbed my neck, and I explained all my nerves and irrational thoughts in a long rambling stream of incoherent half sentences. He said it was okay and that he could sit there with me as long as I needed him to. I loved him for doing that; his patience and his willingness to sit this one out with me was all I needed to hear to go back into the theater. Knowing that going back inside would be on my own terms, and something I genuinely wanted to do with no pressure to do so, made the decision so much easier to make. He smiled at me and asked, "You ready?" as he cocked his head towards the theater doors. I confidently responded "Yes," with a smile that I didn't have to force. I took his hand in mine and we headed back into the theater.

I remember the overwhelming feeling of gratitude I felt in that moment for Tanner's spirit and the role it played in the mending of my own. While most guys would stare up at the lip of that skyscraper, my feet dangling from the edge of my panic attack, Tanner climbed all 50 flights of stairs just to rub my back until I stepped back down on my own accord. No false promises of "things will get better" or desperately pleading for me to come back down to "normal" with him. He saw me, and my panic attack, and did what no other man has ever dared to do: he sat in it with me. Unafraid of the storm that was swirling around me with its black clouds, unforgiving winds and no end in sight, he weathered it with me until it eventually passed, as all storms do. I watched our hands swaying together in the hall, and I wondered if his hands felt heavier to him now that they had absorbed my black clouds like a sponge. Tanner caught me staring at his hands, smiled encouragingly, and opened the door for me. He led the way back to our seats through the pitch blackness.

As soon as our eyes had adjusted, we were entranced by what was playing out on the screen as two velociraptors duked it out on the roof of an old rustic mansion. With my eyes still fixed on the screen, I heard a commotion happening about five inches in front of me. I don't know how it happened, but in the flashes of light projecting off the giant screen, I had seen Tanner trip and almost dive headfirst into a giant trash can, nearly knock it over, and then snatch it back up just before it smacked the linoleum floor. I instinctively reached for Tanner's shirt because in that moment, from my limited point of view, all I could see was him being swallowed up into a tall black hole that we must not have seen when we first walked in. After my brain eventually put together that it was a trash can, not a black hole, and that Tanner had just smacked right into it like a cartoon stepping on a rake, I couldn't hold myself together. Tanner and I dissolved into a fit of choking and stifled laughter.

It wasn't pretty. I'm talking, coughing and choking on our own throats laughing so hard but also trying to laugh quietly because you don't want to be those people in a movie theater that just punted a 4-foot-tall trash can and are now laughing maniacally about it. As I sit in my grandpa's chair now rewriting this memory, I am in tears remembering Tanner desperately trying to stand the trash can back up before it could clatter to the tacky floor with a look of terror on his face. Whatever shred of anxiety that was left clinging to my sleeve in that moment had been shaken free along with the remnants of that trash can.

My graceful, athletic and coordinated Tanner had finally proved he was human, and I only fell deeper in love with him for it. That was the hardest I had ever laughed while on a date. I wanted to laugh like that, with that man, every day until my last day on Earth. It was intoxicating.

We were still choking on our laughter by the time we found our seats next to Jenna again. Tanner made sure that I had the aisle seat, and I rolled my eyes like this was a ridiculous thought but we both knew I was grateful for the gesture. Jenna leaned across Tanner's armrest to ask what happened and if I was okay. I laughed and whispered "Yes, Tanner just tackled the trash can" before I realized she was referring to my panic attack, not Tanner's episode of dancing with the can and she gave me a confused nod. I would have to explain that one after the movie was over.

I directed my attention back up to the screen just in time to catch the last twenty minutes or so of the movie. After a beat or two, my anxiety started to seep back into the corners of my mind and my knee began to jiggle uncontrollably. Tanner subtly reached over and placed his warm hand over my knee without saying a word and I instantly relaxed again. He must have sensed that I didn't want to make a big deal out of this, or he was trying to show that it was no big deal, and he was right here with me. Whatever his intention was, it worked. His sponge-hand had soaked up my anxiety clouds yet again but this time he was aware that they were forming in the first place so he had the time he needed to absorb them before they could destroy another small town in Oklahoma. I watched the remainder of the movie, really watched it, not just putting my eyes on the screen while my mind went to anxiety-land, and I loved every second of it. I silently accepted my victory of staying through the movie while Chris Pratt accepted his own victory on the screen.

Before I knew it, the lights were back on and we were discussing what we thought the little cliffhanger they showed after the credits rolled (yeah, I even made it all the way through the credits, in case anyone at home is keeping score here) was insinuating for the next movie.

We filed out of the theater in pairs and the thick summer air took our breaths away as we emerged back out into the parking lot. The three of us all shared one last round of laughter as I retold the story of Tanner colliding with the trash can as we made our way back to the car. Jenna and I returned Tanner's hoodies as we thanked him again for letting us borrow them. Jenna hit the button on her key fob to unlock her tiny white car, "The Egg", as our family referred to it, and she said her goodbyes to Tanner before ducking to get inside.

I couldn't thank Tanner enough for getting me through that panic attack and even getting me to overcome my fear of sitting through the rest of the movie. He gallantly replied that he didn't really do much, it was all me, and that he was glad he could help. All I could do was smile up at him and finally give into his gravity. I wrapped my arms around his trim waist, and he gently kissed me goodbye. Tanner opened my door and asked me to text him when we got home safely, and we promised we would. With the gentle click of the car door closing behind me, we were on our way back to my house. I never even realized Tanner's hoodie was still in my arms until we were already on the road again; he had made sure it stayed in my hands when he kissed me goodbye. So sneaky, that one.

❋ ❋ ❋

We had barely pulled out of the parking lot when Jenna exploded with "Oh my gosh I really like him!!!!!!!! What happened while you were gone?!" and I filled her in on my panic attack episode. She looked at me and said, "You know, I got your text about the panic attack before Tanner read his, so I showed it to him and without hesitation, he just got up and went out to find you." I had to turn my head out towards my window to hide my bashful smile from Jenna. So that's how Tanner ended up being the one to come out to my rescue; he was worried about me. No one, other than my mother, had ever demonstrated that knee-jerk reaction to ensure my safety and I was so touched I didn't know how to respond. The rest of the car ride home is blurry to me because I was too busy picturing Tanner jumping up to my rescue. I smiled and thought to myself, *he really must care for me.*

Jenna eased The Egg into my mother's driveway, and I took a deep breath as I prepared to tell her about this man and our fiasco of a date that Jenna had just witnessed. Jenna was staying the night again so my mom would be expecting a full report on this mystery man called Tanner. Jenna and I walked in, left our shoes by the door, told my mom how good the movie was, and without further ado, my mother blurted out "So Jenna, did we like him?!" I rolled my eyes and slumped against the couch as I realized my input was no longer needed for this conversation despite the use of the word "we." Jenna explained that she really liked Tanner and that he was such a gentleman for lending us his hoodies, and that he was great with me during my panic attack.

At that last part, I saw my mother wince. It makes my mom sad when I have panic attacks because, I believe, she thinks it's her fault that I have them since they are hereditary. My mom hasn't had a panic attack (that I know of) in almost twenty years, and I know she so badly wants me to get to that point too, but I just can't seem to shake them. I know that scares her.

She peppered Jenna and I with a few more questions about Tanner until she was satisfied, and we were finally allowed to retire to our rooms. I tucked myself deep under the covers and finally texted Tanner to let him know that we had made it home safely and that my mom and cousin seemed to approve of him so far. He replied quickly saying he was also home and that he had a lot of fun with the two of us tonight. We trailed off into a conversation that included me apologizing, yet again, for my panic attack and for being such a "weirdo" that I couldn't even make it through a simple movie. I also thanked him for the millionth time for being there for me and having so much patience for something he couldn't entirely understand. I always assume people see someone with an anxiety disorder as a burden because it feels like such a burden to me; I can only imagine how annoying it is for someone who may not understand the severity of it. Tanner replied with the sweetest text I have ever received; I still have it saved in my phone because it melts my heart every time, I read it:

"I'm happy I could help! Honestly, I don't think of myself as being helpful in those situations, but I feel better knowing you're comfortable so I'll do anything I can when I can. I don't care what I miss out on, I'm happy rubbing your back and talking and even just listening at times. I don't know exactly what goes on in your head during those moments but I'm damn curious about it.

Just remember to breathe in and breathe out like your therapist showed you and never forget that other people don't matter! Who cares who may be watching? It's not about them. Their opinions [of your panic attack symptoms] in that moment don't matter. Let them be 'normal'. I'll be 'weird' with you any day lol. Even if it means I have to dance with a trash can from time to time."

I had never felt so deeply cared for by a man as I did after I read that message. Never having met my father, I had a hard time believing that I could be loved by a man (daddy issues) and my past relationships tended to showcase that. I was often cheated on, lied to, verbally abused, and manipulated into believing I wasn't good enough. So much so that I began to believe that was just what being in a relationship entailed. I had experienced nurturing love before, but it never lasted long, nor did it seem sincere. I always felt like the affection and courtship was just to get in my pants or to shut me up during an argument, but with Tanner, his heart was genuine. I never doubted that for a second. I had fantasized of a love where the adoration went both ways, but I always came up short. Tanner made me reconsider everything I knew about "love." Mutual respect and patience, so much patience, were what I craved, and it oozed from Tanner endlessly. They say there's a lid for every pot and with him, I finally felt the rubber ends seal around my metal rim; my perfect lid plopping perfectly onto my head.

I didn't even know how to respond to his text, and I still don't remember what I ended up saying but I'm sure it didn't compare to his beautiful sentiment. I never thought that a day that I had a panic attack would be a day I would one day so badly wish I could return to. That was the night that I learned having a panic attack does not always insinuate a horrible day. It ended up being one of the best days of my life that I look fondly back on now when I begin to feel anxious again.

When someone genuinely cares for who you are, who you truly are to your core, you begin to shine differently, and life becomes something you can't wait to live fully. I wanted Tanner to be threaded through every single fabric of my life from that moment on. I knew I had found someone remarkable and a connection that could never be replicated. As familiar as the freckle on the back of my left hand, and yet still as new to me as the path by the river, Tanner had somehow become home to me. And let me tell you, it felt good to finally be home.

7

A few days after our movie date, I began to hear less and less from Tanner. My stomach began to rot with the feeling that he was beginning the inevitable process of slowly pulling away that so many others had done in the past. I recognize the pattern before it even begins, almost as if I can sense it coming. I had had a rough day at work, and it had been almost a week since I had seen Tanner. I was beginning to wilt. That sounds dramatic but I could feel my body beginning to fold in on itself without him. Panic crept in around every wall I had only just cemented into place five days ago in that dingy movie theater.

I continued to reach out to Tanner and his responses shrunk down to one word here and an excuse there until finally I couldn't take it anymore. I told him to meet me by the river because we needed to talk. I needed closure if I was ever going to recover from this impending goodbye. Things seemed so perfect between us; I couldn't understand why he was giving me the cold shoulder now.

Tanner's response never came that day. Not the next day, nor the day after that either. I asked him if everything was okay on the sixth day and still there was no response. I felt sick because I knew he was planning his grand exit. Silvy assured me that he was probably just abnormally busy or maybe something had come up. *This is it,* I thought to myself as I sweated around the edges of my phone. I knew from day one that Tanner would be leaving, but I never let myself imagine what this world would be like without him. It was more than I could handle. He was unlike anything else I had ever experienced before, and I couldn't see how my life would ever be the same again. Or how it could maintain this newfound inertia without the source of the movement for that matter. Tanner made me want to live my life again; he made me want to love again the way I had always dreamt of-without fear.

I could feel it in the air around me though, something was wrong. Something had changed. On the seventh day, I finally got a text back from Tanner and my world caved in around me. I couldn't believe the words that swam in front of me at the brim of my tears. His response read:

"Hey. So I've gotta say what's been weighing on me for a little while now. I feel like I'm wasting your time, I don't know what I want out of this between us, but I just don't see it going much further. I've got a lot to focus on [with joining the military] as is and don't wanna drag you through uncertainty and false promises. It's cliché but I do think you're a great person (you don't need me to tell you that I'm sure) and I'm glad we met but I don't think we should keep trying to do what we've been doing. I'm sorry, I didn't mean to come in the picture and cause any inconveniences, but I just know that it'll only get worse and like I said I'm just wasting your time. I'm sorry but I'm just trying to be honest."

I hurled my phone across the room and exploded into ugly, and painful sobs while leaning against my mom's living room couch for support. My heart felt like it had been lit on fire and I struggled to grapple with the aftermath. My first thought was *No. No he can't do this. He can't take the easy way out and throw away this dream that we've built together; it's not fair.*

I scrambled over to my phone and desperately dialed his number but there was no answer. How could he be gone already? I didn't even get to say goodbye. I knew he was pulling away, but I thought it would be more of a slow burn and less of a Band-Aid rip. I thought I had more time. If I was being honest with myself, I thought I could make him stay. I thought he would realize that what we had was something so rare that it couldn't just be tossed back into the universe.

I'm so stupid was my second thought. More hot tears spilled over onto my leggings as I shook my head with embarrassment. *How could you think that he would give up his dreams for you? You thought he was going to stay in this college town and love you forever when you can't even sit through a simple movie or get on a plane?* All the negative thoughts came flooding back like a dam had been broken. I felt so stupid for falling as hard as I did for him when clearly it wasn't reciprocated. Now Tanner was gone, and there was nothing I could do to make him stay this time.

I don't remember the exact text I replied with, but it was something along the lines of: "Don't do this, don't you dare do this. You can't give up on us, we have something incredible right here, in the palm of our hands Tanner and you know it." and then, after growing angrier, "You are a coward Tanner. How could you do this? This is not like you to take the easy way out. Anything this real would've been worth fighting for but you're too afraid. What happened to being fearless?!"

I was flying through all the different emotions faster than my brain could keep up with. I didn't know what to do with myself so I did the only logical thing I could think of doing - I filled a water bottle up with Pinot Grigio and headed to the river. My logical choices are clearly not as logical as the average person. Since I couldn't be near Tanner, I went to the next best thing. The river symbolized Tanner for me now, only the river would always be there, right where I had left it. It would always be there even when Tanner couldn't, or wouldn't be, I should say. The crooked paths aligned with his smile and the rushing water matched his heartbeat against my own when we held each other in the rain. I wanted the river to tell me why Tanner was doing this, so I gave the river all the pain that I could no longer give to Tanner.

I walked the path for hours. I wanted to walk until I couldn't feel my legs anymore; until I couldn't feel anything anymore. I couldn't lose Tanner; I didn't want to go back to the world that Tanner didn't exist in. This new world was so much more colorful than the old one. There were colors in this world that he had painted for me that I never used to see. The soft color of hope, the vibrant color of fearlessness, the bold color of trust, and the most beautiful color of all, unexplainable love. It was unlike a palette I could've ever imagined. I ached for these colors to paint my skies and drench my landscapes for as long as I could keep them. I never wanted my days to be painted with the dull colors of fear, loneliness, and self-doubt ever again but already I could see their familiar hues begin to cloud my world.

I hadn't felt this heartbroken in years. After two hours, I could no longer tell the difference between my tears and my sweat, so I went out to the ledge we sat on the night that we met. I got down to the spot where his hand touched mine and I laid my back against it, both hands covering my heart. It was still there, still beating, somehow. The tears came back, and I cried softly to myself in the same place where I had once thought I'd die of happiness.

As I lay with my back sticking to the stone ledge, Tanner's name came up on my phone again. I almost couldn't bring myself to read his message, I couldn't take any more of his apologies. He asked if we could meet at the river, and I was shocked. Maybe he wanted to finish me off in person? I realized this may be my last chance to see him ever again and that was enough to get me to agree. I told him he knew where to find me. If he had anything else to say to me, I wanted to hear it. I wanted to hear everything and anything he could say to help me make sense of any of this. I was still mad and incredibly hurt, but I would do anything to at least say my goodbye and see him one last time.

Twenty minutes later, I heard Tanner shuffling his way down the ravine and up onto the stone wall. I slowly sat up and watched as he made his way towards me. At first, all I could do was stare at him with a dead face. I wasn't entirely convinced he was going to show up but now that he was here, all of my anger and questions disappeared at the sight of his own forlorn face. I could see in that instant that he was hurt too, and this wasn't what he wanted either. It had never occurred to me that maybe he would be hurting too.

Empathy obscured my pride just long enough for my mouth to ask, "Why'd you do this?"

Tanner hung his head in defeat. If this was an act, he deserved an Oscar. I was both terrified and curious about what he was going to say next. I wanted him to take it all back and sweep me up as he showered me with promises to never do this again, but I knew those odds were not in my favor. He took a long haggard breath and said "Because you're right, Baleigh. I am a coward, and I did take the easy way out." I wasn't satisfied with this answer just yet.

Eventually Tanner disclosed that he had been told he couldn't join the army, but the Navy had said that they wanted him. He was signing a SEAL contract in November, and he would be gone for six years. There was no way this relationship would last and if it did, it could never be a healthy one. I knew he was right, but I couldn't bring myself to admit it. I couldn't go through another long military relationship so quickly after ending a previous one. It had all but done me in the first time; I would never make it a second time.

We both sat there and dejectedly watched the river rush below us. There had to be another way, something I could do or say. As we sat there in our silence, it had grown dark outside, and nighttime had crept into the cracks of our breaking hearts. It was a full moon again and all I could think was *This is where we began and now this is where we will end.* I looked over at Tanner and said "Well we better at least enjoy this time. Before November comes." I didn't know how else to tell him that I accepted his decision, but I wasn't ready to let go quite yet. I couldn't walk these trails or drive these roads knowing Tanner was close to me but no longer in my life. I wanted every last minute he could give to me.

Seeming to read my mind, Tanner finally smiled a shy smile at me in understanding. He reached out for my hand and asked, "Do you wanna go for a swim?" That was not at all what I thought he was going to say. I looked at him with confusion, "Now? In the dark?" and he laughed in response in a way that conveyed "Well, yeah obviously right now" like this was the most normal thing in the world to propose. With Tanner, anything goes. There was nothing left to lose, we were sitting ducks, so why not enjoy the last minutes we had until the lethal trigger was pulled? *C'est La Vie* or whatever. I laughed too and mirrored his smile. Giving in, I said "Sure, why not?" and I took his hand as he led me off the wall and back up the ravine yet again.

I had no idea what the future held for Tanner and me, but I knew I would never take another moment with him for granted. There was no point in wallowing around waiting for the day that we had to say goodbye when we still had the whole summer at our fingertips. As we headed further down the path, I stopped in my tracks and pulled Tanner back with me. I looked him dead in the eyes and said "Tanner, I know we've only been seeing each other about a month or so now and this is going to be really hard come November, but I need you to know it's worth it to me. It sounds crazy but I feel like you were made for me. I feel it deep in my bones in a way that I can't explain. I'll take all the time you'll give me."

Tanner's smile grew sad, and a wave of gratitude washed over his face. He waited a moment and then all at once he closed the distance between us, grabbed both sides of my face with his hands and kissed me with every ounce of emotion he was feeling. It felt like he was thanking me, or maybe he was just so painfully sorry to hurt me like he knew he was going to have to in the fall that he was trying to give back all the time he felt he would be taking from me. He held my face in his hands like it was all that was holding him together and just before he could go to pieces, he let go and shifted the conversation to something a little safer. To something that we could control for the time being that wouldn't utterly shatter our hearts.

"Come on, my swimming spot is right at the bottom of this bike path" and he took my hand to lead me to the spot. He was so excited to show me this place. It reminded me of a giddy child leading his mother to see the picture he had painted in the dining room. It was adorable, but all at once

it hit me that we were about to swim in the Cuyahoga River, in a public park, at ten o'clock at night.
I could already picture coming home in a cop car
(not for the first time) and having to explain this
one to my mother. As I saw Tanner peel his shirt
off, I decided it would be well worth it. I followed
him blindly yet again into the darkness.

8

Despite the dry white wine sloshing around in my water bottle and even more-so in my brain, I can still remember that late-night swim with such clarity. I can still feel the precise temperature of the cool water that was flowing over my arms. I can remember exactly where, in the sky, the full moon was positioned. I know exactly which branch on the decaying tree stump Tanner draped his T-shirt over. It was one of the most memorable moments of my life, and it was also one of the quietest moments I can remember spending with another human. Words had escaped us by then and we let our emotions do all the talking for us over the dull roar of the current.

After Tanner had strewn his shirt over the branch, he began to wade into the black water of the river and find his footing carefully along the rocky bank. I glanced up at the full moon and let it amaze me yet again. There's just something so ethereal and contradictory about a glowing body of water floating in the middle of an otherwise black sky. It takes my breath away every time.

I took a moment to take everything in and study the path Tanner had taken so I could carefully mimic each step. The visibility was relatively clear thanks to the full face of the moon, so I decided it was safe for me to follow him down. The one thing about that night that always strikes me as odd is that it never occurred to me to take my own shirt off. I had a sports bra underneath my tank top so it would have made more sense to leave something dry to come back to, but I suppose I was too swept up in the moment to think of that.

As I began my own descent deeper into the flowing river, Tanner broke the silence and exclaimed "Oh God I just felt a fish!" and I froze in hopes that maybe the fish would spare my own legs from its scaley caress. Realizing that the fish would have been long past me once it had gotten to Tanner, I began to laugh at his expense. For someone who adored the water as much as Tanner did, he sure was jumpy when a tiny little fish brushed against him. Still teasing him about the big bad fish that he narrowly escaped being attacked by, I waded deeper to close the distance between us.

Tanner reached out for my hand to help pull me in closer against the current. We found our footing and admonished at the fact that now it was time to face one another, to face our truths. He wrapped his arms around my waist, and I placed my own arms around his neck. We bobbed along together like that with the waves of the river, just taking each other in, for quite some time. It occurred to me then that I had never seen Tanner this close in the light before. The raw vulnerability of staring into another person's eyes for a prolonged period can answer so many questions and reveal everything about a person's heart. I saw so much sadness in Tanner's face that it broke my heart. I imagined it broke his heart too, seeing the same look mirrored on my own face. I could see he was more apologetic than he could verbally describe but his telling eyes disclosed all of this to me, whether he meant for them to or not. It was truly hurting him to have to leave me.

I couldn't bear to look the truth in the eye any longer so I pulled him as close to me as I could and rested my cheek on his shoulder. I didn't waste the moment wondering what he was thinking, or what would happen next. I closed my eyes and relished in the feeling of his damp shoulder pressed against my cheek while the current rhythmically rocked us closer and further away from each other. It was a slow dance that the river created for us, moving our bodies so that we wouldn't have to. I quietly thanked our river for allowing us this moment together. I knew I would never take it for granted and even in my darkest days, the memory of this slow dance in the river with Tanner is what keeps me going.

The weightlessness of our bodies buoying in the river felt like a dream. I was being held and floating away at the same time, Tanner's arms never letting me stray too far from his body. This closeness and intimacy were what I had been craving from Tanner for weeks now. To hold him and never let go would be ideal, but this moment, this was as close I would ever get to that. We were alone and in our own little world, so I allowed my eyes to close against his chest again. *Drink this in, remember every detail of this moment, Baleigh* my subconscious mind chided me gently. *Carry this night with you when you miss him more than you think you can bear.*

Slowly reopening my eyes and forcing myself back into reality before I began to cry, I peeled my cheek from his shoulder and looked up towards Tanner's face again. Before I could even read and make sense of his expression, his lips were pressed to mine. It started out slowly at first and gradually grew to be an act of purpose and unrequited passion. It was as if we had unlocked a raw hunger in one another that had been hidden beneath our puppy-lust. Tanner kissed me like he was searching for something, like he couldn't hold himself back anymore. I kissed him back just as forcefully because this felt more like a goodbye than an awakening and I refused to ruin this moment with my brimming tears.

The fierceness of Tanner's kisses convinced my body to take over. My hands slipped under the water to grab his lower back and press him harder to me, my nails carved little half-smiles into his skin. His hands were wrapped around my neck and neither of us could bring each other close enough. Suddenly, his lips just weren't enough for me, and I found my mouth moving down his neck and back to his shoulders where just seconds ago, my cheek had laid. I wanted to know what every part of Tanner's body felt against my own and it's hard to stop me once I start that journey.

Eventually, Tanner himself pulled away from me in a sad attempt to slow things down. There are a lot of fun activities to do in the Cuyahoga River, but sex is not one of them. Lord knows what lurks in the river that caught fire, and nobody needs that in their nether regions. I stared up at him with my red and, now swollen, lips for an answer to an unasked question. Tanner read my expression and said "I don't live far from here if you want to come over for a bit? No pressure though, you totally don't have to." I was taken aback by this for a moment as he had never offered to have me over to his house before. My body flushed at the thought of finally getting a glimpse into his life outside the river.

I laughed at his bashful chivalry and began to make my way back to the embankment as an answer to his proposition. Once we were back on dry land and walking up to our cars, Tanner told me just to follow him back to his place and apologized in advance for the lack of furniture because he was in the process of moving.

It occurred to me that my clothes and I were completely soaked, and I had begun to shiver. Tanner assured me that he had some sweats I could change into once we got there so I just cranked the heat in my car in the meantime. It was a short drive to the quaint little house he was renting with another roommate and her cat. The cat greeted us at the door, and I of course had to stop and pet him and make him my new best friend like the crazy cat lady that I am. After we became besties and promised to add each other on Facebook, I said goodbye to the cat and so I could change into some dry clothes.

Tanner led me down the hall towards his room, showing me the kitchen and the living room briefly on the way, and it was an impressive little place. The floors were new, and the countertops appeared to be granite and very clean. Cleanliness is very important to me, so I mentally checked that off my list as we entered his barren room. There was no TV, no decorations, no dresser - just a giant king-sized bed that took up most of the bedroom. The massive red comforter looked so warm and cozy it took all that I had to not immediately dive in and wrap myself in it. Tanner handed me a sweatshirt and a pair of sweatpants from somewhere out of my eyeline and modestly ducked out to let me change in private. The chivalry with this one never ceased to amaze me, but I was still on fire from our impromptu make out session in the river.

After I changed into his dry clothes, I sat on the bed and waited for him to come back into the room. Tanner strolled in wearing his own pair of dry sweatpants and a bare chest. In the harsh light beaming from the ceiling fan, I finally got a good look at him and the tattoos that decorated his body. The right side of his ribs had a large tattoo that ran from near his armpit down to his hip and appeared to read the word "Live" only the letters were spelled out with weapons. The "L" was a pistol, the "I" were nunchucks, the "V" was a switchblade, and the "E" was some sort of rifle or machine gun. I made another mental note to ask him what the significance of his tattoo was other than the subliminal message behind it. I had already seen the rest of his tattoos but now I had a moment to look at the small details of his black panther and Jungle book themed sleeve. These artifacts on his body paired with his tanned skin were making it nearly impossible not to reach out and pull him back to me.

It was all too soon that Tanner had put a clean shirt on, and I couldn't help myself as I said, "Wow you should not wear a shirt more often" and he modestly shook his head and laughed in response. I watched as he pulled two metal hangers from the empty closet and hung up his wet towel. He turned around to me and said "Don't judge me, but I hang up my towels on hangers. It's just something I do." I assured him that I wouldn't judge him, but I was laughing at the sight of it without realizing I was doing it. I mean, who hangs their towels on hangers?

Finally, Tanner joined me on the bed and began scrolling through his phone as he said to me "I know you sleep with the TV on, but I obviously don't have one in here, so I'll play some music. What would you like to hear?" I was touched that he had remembered that detail about my sleep habits and instantly embarrassed for thinking he would be joining me in this bed for any other reason than to just be closer to me. Remembering that Tanner was a gentleman was hard to do when I had become accustomed to men acting like dogs.

Coming back to his question, I answered that one of my absolute favorite artists of all time, Brandi Carlile, had released a new album earlier that year. The way Brandi's voice drips with earnestness sells the lyrics completely. You can feel her pain and her joy coming through the speakers like you're right there experiencing it with her. The acoustic guitars pluck at your heartstrings and the pianos sift through your memories and bring the sharpest ones to the surface. It was so beautiful that I couldn't stop listening to it on repeat for months so naturally, I asked Tanner to play the album "By the Way, I Forgive You." As the opening chords to "Every Time I Hear That Song" began to play over the speaker, I snuggled up closer to Tanner and he folded his arms around me again. I was nervous that Brandi might not be his cup of tea but he never told me otherwise so I assumed he was just as soothed by her music as I was.

Engulfed in the intimacy of this moment, I leaned in and kissed the side of Tanner's face and as he lay there exhausted with a playful smile on his face. "Mmm, I could get used to this" he said, lightly laughing with his eyes closed. I told him I could too as I rested my head on his chest. I think we were both enjoying the make-believe world we had created for ourselves. A world where Tanner's dreams didn't take him so far from me; a world where we could be together for as long as we wanted. Ignorance is bliss. It's dangerous, but blissful, nonetheless.

We lay there together and listened to Brandi's soul-soothing voice lull us into a meditative state. The song ended and I opened my sleepy eyes as I whispered, "Don't leave me like that again, okay?" I felt Tanner's chest rise as he took in what I had said and replied "I'm sorry. I won't ever try to leave you like that again." Somewhere deep down inside I knew that was something he couldn't promise me. However, that wasn't enough for me, so I said, "You promise?" He kissed my forehead as he said, "I promise, Baleigh." As if on cue, Brandi Carlile sang in her sultriest of voices "*I loved you the first time I saw you, and you know I love you still"* from her song Party of One. I let a small smile come over me and I settled in closer to Tanner while I waited for sleep to come. Whether Tanner intended to keep his promise or not, I didn't care. Right now, he was all mine. That was all I could ask for.

About halfway through the album, Tanner began to snore softly. It wasn't a loud dad-snore, it was more of a forcing of his breath through tightly pressed lips. I almost wanted to part his lips for him so he could exhale more easily but obviously that was not an option, so I focused my attention back to Brandi. I always find myself being so envious of how quickly men can fall asleep. I have to be in the exact right position, with TV at the perfect volume, with the room at just the right temperature.

The last chord of the final song on the album faded out and I was left with nothing but my thoughts and Tanner snoring in my ear to coax me to sleep. I faded in and out, but I knew I wasn't going to last much longer; this was usually the time when my anxiety began to kick in, and I got antsy. Tanner had been asleep for an hour, maybe two when I tried to slip out from under his grasp. Even in his sleep, he could sense the second there was a trace of distance between us and unconsciously pulled me back into him.

This was the sweetest thing I had ever seen an unconscious man do, but I knew my time to escape was running out and panic was edging in. I hesitantly pulled away again, this time not as carefully, in hopes that he would rouse himself and realize I was leaving. Tanner didn't open his eyes, so I whispered "Hey. Tanner? I'm sorry, but I have to go now." He responded with that guttural grunt men always make when they're barely awake, but they can sense that you asked them a question. He didn't seem to register what I had said so I repeated myself as I sat up fully and this time, he grunted but in the shape of the word "Why?" I smiled at the fact that he didn't want me to leave. Regret was dripping from my voice as I explained "Because anxiety said so." Another grunt. Then, "Are you sure? Do you have to?" Poor sweet man, he was breaking my heart with his earnest desire to keep me next to him. I said I was sure I had to leave and that I didn't want to leave at all, but this was something I didn't yet have the strength to control.

Nighttime anxiety is far worse than daytime anxiety. I don't know why but there's no coming back from a nighttime panic attack, at least not for me. So, this was one anxiety cloud that Tanner wouldn't be able to clear from my head by dancing with a trash can. The feeling of my fight-or-flight ripping through my chest was unbearable. I knew I would lie there for hours, my stomach rolling and my body sweating with fear if I didn't go home now. I wanted nothing more than to wake up beside him in the morning but not even a tranquilizer could knock me out when I was feeling like this. Experience showed me that there's not much more that I can do without emergency-use medication like Xanax or Klonopin to calm me down when I'm away from home. Unfamiliar settings set my nerves on fire, especially when I know I should be sleeping and relaxed.

Tanner said that he understood and told me to drive home safely. I told him I would text him once I got home and that he should get some sleep. With one last lingering kiss on his cheek, I left that beautiful man alone in his bed and it killed every molecule in my body to do it. If my anxiety was a person, I would have punched it in its ugly face at that moment. Cursing my churning stomach, I slinked through the house to grab my keys and my phone before saying goodbye to the friendly kitty and getting into my car. My seat was still soaked but I felt instant relief once I was on the road and headed to my own bed; another panic attack successfully averted.

My drive home was a quick ten-minute commute given that there wasn't any traffic at 4 a.m. in Kent, Ohio. The best (sarcasm) part was that when I finally crashed into my own familiar sheets with my own familiar cats, I was already wishing I was still lying next to Tanner just as I had suspected I would. Too late now, just another moment stolen by my anxiety. With regret also came instant relief, however. Familiarity works just as well as Klonopin for me sometimes.

I was too exhausted to feel sorry for myself, so I texted Tanner to let him know that I had made it home safely and almost immediately fell into a sleep so deep that only a dead hamster could replicate.

9

I woke up the next morning feeling like the world was slanted a little too far to the left; everything was virtually the same, but there was one fine hair out of place. I knew what this meant, my anxiety was overthinking my life for me, and a panic attack was about to jump out from around the corner. The reality of the night before sat heavy on my chest during my short drive to work. The romance of my river dance from the night before had faded and the hard questions I had avoided asking myself started throwing sucker punches at me. Did I really want to be in another military relationship again? Starting from scratch? I would be 31 by the time Tanner finished his contract and I was only 24 now. I've watched the military take a boy and turn him into a jaded and bitter man; could I watch the same thing happen to Tanner? All the missed birthdays, anniversaries and Christmases that broke my heart as a teenager, would they still sting just as badly in adulthood? It was only four months ago that I was packing up my drug-deal Chapstick and checking out of a mental health facility with shaky hands.

Was this really the best time to enter a strained relationship? Maybe Tanner was right when he said this could never work. The dread and the doubt crept in.

For every worry and "what if" that my anxiety threw at me, my heart countered with "on the other hand, would you really want to live your life any other way than with Tanner somehow in it?" And all at once I would find myself having to decide what would be worse; a couple of Christmases without Tanner or possibly the rest of my life without him. I knew I had my answer then, and I knew I would do anything to keep Tanner in my life, whether that meant romantically or platonically. I would trade all my birthdays and Christmases to be with Tanner for even just one random April morning in the future.

The weight of realizing I would in some way or another be saying goodbye to Tanner soon, coupled with the stifling heat, and the thought of a panic attack at my new job threw me drastically into an unforgiving anxiety hole. In a lame attempt at calming myself down I started to think *Okay Baleigh, get it together, we don't have panic attacks at work anymore* and in a matter of minutes I was grabbing my purse and heading home to have my panic attack in peace. Self-soothing is near the top of the list of things that I am not good at, along with dieting and simple math.

On my way home, I called Tanner with high hopes that he could help me come down from my self-inflicted hysteria once again. I knew it wasn't fair to appoint him as my new organic form of Klonopin but the relaxing impact he had on me was as addictive, if not more so, than the pills themself. I was itching for my next hit of Tanner. However, there was no answer on the other end of the line. He was working, but he still managed to text back a quick "Hey, sorry I'm working. Everything okay?" I felt like I was being too needy or that my anxiety was starting to become a nuisance to him, so I waited a while before typing back "Yeah, just another stupid panic attack. Meet by the river later for a walk?"

I then plopped on the couch to take a nap and wash out all the residual panic in my body while I waited for his response. When I woke up, Tanner had answered, and we decided to meet for a "relaxing" evening walk by our river after dinner. Any remaining pressure in my chest lifted and with the thought of being next to him again soon, I immediately felt lighter.

When I pulled my little Sonata into the parking lot by the railroad tracks, I was surprised to see Tanner standing there waiting for me; I was usually the first one to arrive when we met. He, of course, was wearing his toe-shoes and his pocket-sized smile. I could feel that today was not going to be an ordinary walk along the river, and I wasn't sure how I felt about that. I had barely gotten out of the car and hugged Tanner before he said

"Today, we're talking about your fears. Anxiety stems from fear, so we're going to come to terms with your rational, and irrational fears."

I slowly started to sit back down in the driver's seat in response to his proposition and Tanner interjected "Oh no, we're doing this! You'll feel better, I promise!" My first thought? *This was a trap.* It made sense that he saw a problem and wanted to fix it. Tanner was a practical man and if he was presented with an obstacle, he was going to overcome it. While I was immediately terrified, I was also touched that he wanted me to soak up every drop of life that I had left ahead of me. To him, that meant ditching the fears in my head that held me down like sandbags and jumping headfirst into the things that make most people feel alive. I was thankful to have the safety net that was his hand to hold on the way down.

I wasn't sure if I liked the mischievous look in Tanner's eye, but I took his hand and let him lead me towards our river anyway. There were way too many people milling around for him to attempt to throw me off a bridge or swallow fire or something equally as crazy that people have done to conquer their fears.

I was lagging behind today because I was afraid of what Tanner had in mind, so I had to strain to hear him say, "Let's start with this, what are your top three biggest fears?" I chewed on my lip and thought for a moment before answering.

No one had ever asked me this before. However, my fears swirled around in my skull so often that I didn't have to think long before answering, "Heights, my mom dying, and flying." I answered confidently. Tanner took a minute to mull that over and decided, simply "You are not afraid of flying or heights, you are afraid of falling, or more simply: dying. You fear death. For you, and your mother." I had never thought of my fears as objectively as this before, but I had to admit, it did make sense. He was painfully correct in his analysis.

This realization felt like defeat to me though because that meant I was not as strong in my faith in God as I claimed to be. If I truly believed in the paradise that is Heaven, why wouldn't I want that for myself and for the people that I loved? Uncertainty is the root of all evil and this was no different. Anxiety will make you question everything. Some days you'll be convinced that the grass isn't green and that everything you were taught as a child was a lie. It's not so much paranoia as it is dissociation from reality. Even when you know something to be factual, anxiety will slip in through the cracks and whisper into your ear *"Is it really though? How do you even know that? Where did that fact come from?"*

"Okay yeah, but isn't everyone afraid of dying?" I hesitantly replied to Tanner. Tanner stopped so hard in his tracks I almost lost my balance trying not to rear-end him (mind out of the gutter!) He gaped at me and sputtered, "No. Fearing death is like fearing that a movie is going to an end or that the sun will rise tomorrow. It's inevitable, so there's no point in fearing it. Most people believe in an afterlife or a higher power, so they trust that death is not really 'the end'."

I shrugged and fought the urge to roll my eyes as I thought *Ugh, here we go*. Tanner read my expression and redirected his thoughts. Starting over, he said, "I know you're religious so don't you trust that you and your mom will both just go to heaven together?" I knew that question was coming, so I already had my reply ready and perched on the tip of my tongue.

"Of course, I do." I said, "But I guess I'm more afraid of what happens before then, 'on the way down' so to speak. I'm afraid death will hurt or be the most terrifying thing I've ever experienced. I'm also afraid that I can't physically or mentally function in a world without my mother."

I've always had this thought but until that moment, I had never said it aloud or given it permission to come to life. Thinking of the world without my mother in it physically makes me sick. I've never known how to keep myself afloat without her. It's always just been the two of us and when my anxiety comes crashing in around me, she's the only one who can make the world feel like a safe place again. She puts the ground back under my feet when I'm mid freefall.

To me it would feel like I suddenly live in a world where medicine, hospitals, and doctors no longer exist. You are on your own to keep yourself alive and you better not fuck up because there's no one there to catch you when you fall anymore. My mom has always felt like the other half of me; where my personality ends, hers begins and what I lack, she has in abundance. There is no love out there for me like the love my mother has for me, and I'm not entirely convinced that my body would keep breathing, pumping my blood, or moving without the presence of her soul on this planet. You hear the stories of spouses and mothers "dying" of a broken heart and I've always felt deep in the marrow of my bones since I was child, that I would die when my mother died. That would crush her of course, she's told me a million times before "I would still always be with you" but that's never comforted me like she intends it to. I know that losing my mother is inevitable, but I like to think that I'll be so old by then that I won't be far behind her, or I'll be too old to know the difference.

Tanner was close with his mother too, so I was hoping he could at least understand that last part of my answer. Again, he took his time to let my answer resonate and finally he said "You will never be dealt anything that you can't handle, and when you do go, it will be because it is truly your time. It all happens when it's supposed to happen so you might as well trust in the universe or 'God'.

They know what they're doing."

It was easier said than done but I knew he was right. Who was I to say that I knew better than God and/or the universe when it comes to the fate of my mother, or for myself for that matter? I hated how many clichés he had used to describe his reasoning, but I understood what he was trying to convey. I relished in the comfort of knowing that I was exactly where I was supposed to be and so was my mother. And so was Tanner. We walked hand-in-hand, silently along the river for a long time after that. Both of us were digesting the conversation separately in our own ways.

After crossing over the shit bridge, we were now entering the small tunnel that sat underneath the railroad track bridge about 60 feet above us. The bridge was old and rusty and there was a historic plaque nearby that regaled pedestrians with ancient stories of the history of the trains that passed over it many centuries ago. The tracks were still functioning, but it was rare to see a train passing over the trail these days. On the occasion that you did get to spot a train moseying its way over the river, it looked like a dream. Like the cars were floating through the sky to a make-believe destination straight out of a Pixar film.

Tanner looked up to the tracks towering above our heads and said, "We're going to walk across those tracks today." I utterly guffawed right in his face. His tone was so dead-serious that I thought for sure there was no way he was serious.

He was just messing with me! I pitifully thought to myself. *What a little jokester, that Tanner.* I was really trying to convince myself that he was kidding.

There's no way ... he wasn't really ... he couldn't be serious.

"I'm serious," he clarified. Apparently, my confused expression had projected my inner dialogue.

HAH. He was serious! *Oh honey, bless your heart, you really think I'm going to climb up this gravel death trap of a hill to walk across some flimsy railroad bridge in a valiant effort to face my fears? You better skip to my Lou my darling, because there ain't no way. No way. None. That I am getting my happy ass up there.* However, we were still moving toward the bridge, so that was interesting. My body was defying my brain's blatant screams and warnings. I looked at Tanner, fixed my baby face into what I hoped looked like a stern, and parental glare and firmly said "No. Absolutely not. There's no way."

Tanner cocked his head to the side and retorted, "Come on, I've done this a million times. I would never let anything happen to you; you know that. Plus, the view is amazing!"

"No, no, no, a million times, no!" I half-heartedly repeated. *This man is trying to kill me.*

Tanner smiled his stupid Tanner smile and pleaded, "Come on, we're going. You won't regret it. Be careful up the gravel path, it's easy to slip. Follow me." as if he had the last say and the final decision had been made. I sputtered and gawked at him and fought my toughest fight, but I knew I was going to give in. I gave one last glimpse upward towards my fate and exhaled defeatedly as I followed him over to the man-made path. *Well shit,* I thought, *this is happening. We're really doing this. Oh shit. Oh shit.* *Cue the profuse sweating and nervous laughing*

Unfortunately, the loose gravel was tricky to climb up after all; Tanner was right. I have no idea how I made it up, but somehow, I did. Tanner grabbed my hand and helped to heave me up the last couple steps. By the time we reached the top, I was dripping with sweat and laughing maniacally by accident to contain my panic. With an annoyingly triumphant look over the tracks, and a long sweep of his arms, he said "See?! That wasn't so bad! You made it!" I stutter-laughed and said "YepSureDidNowLetsGo" in one hurried breath as I turned to make my way back down the gravel mountain before my heart fell out of my chest.

Tanner caught my arm and laughed at my failed attempt at a kidding-not-kidding remark and a quick exit. I looked to him and made the Tina Belcher "uhhhhhhhh" sound as I realized we were going to walk over the tracks that seemed to be floating in the sky despite my lackluster effort to escape back down the hill. Maybe a tiny part of me wanted to do this after all. I wanted to wake up and feel alive again.

Tanner sensed my haste as I followed slowly behind him, so he started coaching me across the suspended tracks. "Just put one foot in front of the other. Hold my hand, I won't let you go. I promise." He called over his shoulder. *He's done this a million times. He's done this a million times.* I was chanting this in my head like a mantra as I forced my feet to move toward Tanner.

He stopped to wait for me to catch up and I finally gave in and grasped for his hand. I followed him, one foot at a time, across the tracks at a snail's pace. Tanner was patient with me, but he also didn't want me to forget the purpose of this little adventure, so he coaxed, "What are you afraid of right now?"

I was so frustrated with his life lesson that I sarcastically replied with, "Uhh I don't know, maybe falling through one of these slats to my untimely death. Or getting my foot caught and watching as a train turns me into a closed-casket ceremony. The possibilities are endless here Tanner!"

Ignoring my sarcasm, he calmly replied, "These slats are too close together for either of those things to happen. Stop staring at your feet, you're going to make yourself trip." I was so focused on watching my feet that I didn't realize how far out over the bridge we had walked, and I suddenly felt like I was paralyzed.

"I can't! I can't look up, oh my God I can't move!" I said with a hint of hysteria peeking through. Tanner turned around to face me, never dropping my hand, and put his face close to my downward chin as he said "Hey! You're perfectly fine, it's okay. We'll look up at the same time then, okay? I'm right here, I won't let you go. This will all be worth it when you see this view." I allowed Tanner's words to comfort me, and I took a deep breath in. As I exhaled, counted to three, and I lifted my chin into the wind and slowly opened my eyes.

My breath froze in my lungs. I couldn't believe what I saw. It was amazing. It was more than amazing. It didn't even look real. I looked out over a fairytale world from high up in the clouds. We were standing in the middle of the bridge, suspended over the river, and I felt like I could see for miles. Rolling hills, the roaring river, the water plant, the shit bridge, train tracks running in every direction and joggers that looked like Polly Pockets. I felt like I was standing on top of the world and all the air in my lungs was stolen by this beautiful scene unfolding around me. I don't do dangerous things. I'll never sky dive, I've never been on a rollercoaster that goes upside down, and I wear my seatbelt more often than I wear my bra. I've never regretted not being a risk-taker until that moment. I longed then for all the views, thrills, and adventures I had missed out on in the past. I decided, while swaying back and forth ever so slightly on that bridge, that I would stop saying no before considering what beauty could come from saying yes.

I was caught in a dream. I couldn't look away for fear that I may wake up. It occurred to me that I hadn't said anything since I opened my eyes, but I couldn't think of what to say, for once in my life. I was free, I was above all the fears of my modern life. Up here, with Tanner, anxiety didn't exist, and fear wasn't real. I looked at Tanner with my mouth hanging open as a gasp of incredulous laughter escaped me. He wasn't even looking at the world that lay below us, he was just smiling adoringly at me and my reaction. All he could say was "Told ya" as he playfully swung my hand in the air beside him. I adored him so much from this vantage point. I could never thank him enough for giving me this memory that I would always hold close to my heart.

I was still sweating from the adrenaline rush, but my body felt so eerily at peace, like we were floating up there, on the tracks in the sky. I couldn't tear my eyes away from the splendor of it all. I couldn't believe I had almost missed out on this, and I wanted to engrain every square inch in my memory. I looked on for who knows how long, maybe years.

Tanner shook me from my reverie when he finally spoke again. He said, "Not to spoil this moment or cut it too short but I *may have* forgot to mention that this is totally illegal. All those joggers are staring at us like they've got one finger on the "call" button after having just dialed 911 so we should probably go now." He was laughing but I could tell he meant it as a warning. Before I could respond, a siren sounded from somewhere nearby, and we both grabbed onto each other as we tried to hurry back across the tracks. Those same tracks that had almost sent me to an early grave from anxiety were now flying underneath my feet effortlessly. I was smiling wildly as Tanner and I laughed and shrieked in the clouds together. He never let go of my hand, as promised.

We laughed at my clumsy slipping and sliding across the gravel the whole way down the ravine until it finally spit us back out onto the trail in a giggling, sweating mess. The two of us laughed so hard that it took us a minute to catch our breath. Tanner was still doubled over when he looked over at me and said "Oh my God, you're so sweaty! And red! Are you okay?" I knew I had to look like hell, I get tomato-face red when I exercise or when my adrenaline is pumping, and we had just taken part in both of those things. "Shut up, I get sweaty when I'm scared okay!" I laughed as I childishly defended myself.

Still coming down from the high of walking across the train tracks in the sky, we stumbled down towards the river to cool off. I took off my shoes and put my feet in the cool brown water and Tanner soaked his head like a Labrador. He was so at home with the river that it presented as a natural movement for him he had done many times before. He shook the excess water from his shaggy hair and passed his rough hands over his face to wipe the water from his eyes before looking over to me again with a smile.

Without much of a conversation, we moved off the ledge and further down the cement wall to sit closer to the rapids. I planted myself down on a boulder that was jutting from the river so I could sit as close to the river as possible without being submerged. Tanner was further back, lost in his own thoughts, and watching the river flow. Now that we were out of the clouds and back on the ground, reality set back in. November was only four months away; a shadow on the horizon growing larger by the day. Tanner was still leaving soon. He must've been brought back to the sobering fact that he would be gone soon too because he looked over to me and said, in a melancholy tone, "Can I hold you for a while?" Sometimes the sincerity of his words just broke my heart. "Of course," I said as I scooted over on my rock to make room for him.

Making his way over the rocks, Tanner met

me on the boulder and plopped himself in the space behind me. He stretched his legs out around either side of my body and wrapped his arms around my waist, pulling me closer. I tilted my head up to meet his eyes and he rested his chin on my shoulder. Leaning my head back into his chest, I turned my head and held his face with my hand as I kissed his cheek, lingering there for a beat too long. My fingers slid into his thick hair, and he kissed the hair against my head; it was a heartbreaking gesture that I never wanted to end. My heart ached for him. I wanted this forever. It was a feeling of invincibility, like a teenager going too fast in their parent's car; nothing could touch me. Tanner's arms became my force field, and with them around my waist, there was nothing I couldn't overcome. The trust we had just built, 60 feet above the ordinary world below us, was unbreakable. I would hold onto this otherworldly connection to his soul for the rest of my life and cherish it for what it was; my reason to believe in love again. It was more than lust, and a small step past friendship; the best of both worlds all wrapped up into one achingly beautiful man. I kissed another apology onto his soft cheek. I was sorry that we were hurting so much. I was sorry he had to leave me to chase his dreams. I was sorry that time was not on our side.

Tanner jerked his head up, bringing me out of my heart and back to the river. I followed his gaze to see some teenagers haphazardly making their way down the cement wall towards us. Once they saw us all pretzeled together, they began laughing and said "Oh! Don't mind us! Just going for a swim!" They were clearly high; we could smell them even from upwind. We laughed and yelled back "You're good! We're just chilling. Nothing to see here," and the gaggle of them went about chortling to one another as they waded into the river. We watched them playfully struggle against the river current and listened to their cheers of excitement until the sun began to set. Tanner held me for what felt like hours, rubbing tiny circles into my hands with his thumbs absentmindedly.

Tanner eventually took my hand and led me back up the steep incline to the path. We reached the parking lot together and I leaned back against my car as I thanked him for another amazing afternoon. He smiled against my lips and muttered "Anytime. We're going to knock these fears out one by one." he joked. I kissed him back and rolled my eyes as I pulled away. I was saying goodbye, but my hands clutched him even closer to me. He removed my hands from his waist, kissed each one, as he said "I'll see you next time. Bring your passport" with a playful wink.

I was laughing to myself as I drove away from him because even though he was kidding, I knew Tanner really thought he could get me on a plane again (*Not even for front row tickets to a Bon*

Jovi concert I thought. Well...okay maybe for that, but ONLY that) one day. I was almost home when I realized that I had completely forgotten about my panic attack earlier today; the reason why I had called Tanner down to the river in the first place.

10

One thing that I take very seriously is putting a butt-load of pressure on myself for no logical reason. I take this so seriously in fact, that I convince myself everyone around me is constantly judging the things I say and do when, in reality, most of them are just wondering how to pronounce my name (it's like Bay-lee, for those of you who are still unsure). So, when I decided it was time for Silvy to meet Tanner, my brain had told me that there were a lot of high expectations, and everything had to go perfectly. I've spent a good amount of my life talking up the men I've dated to not only my mother, but also to my friends. They can be rather insatiable so getting their approval only became that much more important to me. My mom and all my friends adored my ex-boyfriend and that is the only man they have ever *really* given approval. Granted, I do pick some terrible people to bring around but hello, daddy issues are a thing. Cut me some slack.

I try so hard not to let my friends and family's opinions get to me and be the "fuck what other people say, only you know your relationship" girl but let's be honest, everyone wants their best friend and their mother to like their significant other. It just makes life so much easier and copacetic. Obviously, I had already told Silvy just about everything there was to know about Tanner, but she was still rightfully skeptical. I mean, he was leaving. For like six years. And he could die. And he already broke things off with me once. No pressure, nothing to prove here! The odds were against Tanner before he even had a chance to say hello. Silvy knew I was nervous to have her meet him so she suggested that we all just hangout by the river, where Tanner and I would be more comfortable. She loved a good hike as much as we did so I took her up on her suggestion. I asked Tanner if he would like to go for a walk with us so he could meet my best friend who meant the whole world to me. I was nervous to ask him - what if he thought it was too soon? Or worse yet, what if he thought it wasn't worth it at all since, he would be leaving in a few short months anyway?

Of course, in perfect Tanner fashion, he said he would love to join us. We set a date and time for an evening walk after work when it would be comfortably cool outside.

It was almost dusk when Silvy, in her pearl blue car, met me down by the river. We were a little early, so we decided to start without Tanner; I remember really wanting to get a good hike in before the sun went down in hopes of sweating out some extra calories (and maybe some extra nerves?) before seeing Tanner. Silvy is considerably smaller and skinnier than I am so I was nervous that I would look like an ogre in comparison to her. I knew that wasn't how Tanner saw people, but it was, regrettably, how I saw people. Rather, it was how I saw myself, I should say. Constant envy for your best friend's appearance is another hidden side effect of anxiety; it loves to find new ways of making me think that I am not good enough. I had to repeat a mantra in my head during that entire hike: "*Silvy is not* better. *Silvy is just* different."

Tanner had let me know earlier that he would call me when he was on his way. I made a point to turn the volume up on my phone so I wouldn't miss his call. Silvy and I made it about a mile down the path, but I still hadn't heard anything from Tanner. I pretended like I wasn't getting nervous but inside I was freaking out. As soon as the thought of *He would ditch me when I finally decided to introduce him to Silvy* popped into my mind, I knew I had cursed myself. Another mile went by and still nothing from Tanner.

I finally had to address the elephant on the trail, and I nervously choked out to Silvy, "He must have had to work late, this is so unlike him! I hope he's okay." She assured me it was okay and that these things happened. I said I was sure we would hear something from him any minute as we turned around to make our way back to the parking lot. My heart was in my throat and my stomach was in my butt; I was full of dread. It never occurred to me that Tanner might not show up at all until we were making our way back to the parking lot. How would I ever recover from that? How would *Tanner* ever recover from that? It would take months for Silvy to get past that and be able to see Tanner for the good guy that he truly was.

It was dark out by the time we got back to our cars. Completely embarrassed, drenched in sweat from the long and humid hike, and bummed out, I apologized to Silvy for dragging her out here for nothing about a thousand times. I could tell she was not impressed, and that Tanner had blown it with her. I was frustrated too but mostly just disappointed. I had such high hopes for this night going into it. I had built it up to this magnificent turning point for Tanner and me - *He met my best friend! This must be serious!* - so much so that the devastation was hitting harder than it should have. Silvy suggested we go back to her place and have a few beers with our other friend Emmy to take our minds off the situation. Wanting nothing more than to pound beers until my embarrassment subsided, I agreed to follow Silvy back to her house. I couldn't believe I had just gotten ditched by the man that I had spent months bragging about. I wondered if Silvy thought I had made the whole thing up, or at least fudged some of the numbers. First impressions are everything so it's important to show up for it.

I was blasting Cardi B (don't hate) and angry-crying when Tanner's name finally popped up on my phone, three hours after we were supposed to have met on the trail. All three of his texts came in one after another and my phone dinged relentlessly like a seatbelt sensor. Annoyed and relieved all at once, I glanced at the screen begrudgingly.

In order, they read:

"Baleigh! I just woke up. I'm so sorry. I'm not kidding!"

And then, "I fucking hate naps!"

Followed with, "I did not mean to fall asleep."

A normal person would've replied with something like "It's okay, I know you work outside all day in the heat and must be exhausted. Things happen. Maybe next week instead!" and then everything would've been fine. However, as we have covered, I am not a normal person. I lash out when I get embarrassed or when I'm hurt. I don't know if you've ever heard the saying that "Hungarian blood runs hot" but I can assure that it is a factual phrase. My mother, her father and I all had tempers that ran hot enough to melt rubber.

I was angry that he messed up his first impression with my best friend, but I think I was more terrified to see that the veil had been lifted and Tanner was, despite it all, only human. He was imperfect and he made mistakes. He slept through alarms and missed important events like any other human has done before. My mind translated this as him not caring enough about meeting the people that I loved. *Tanner never misses anything when it comes to me. He's never late. This must not have been as important to him.* My brain was determined to believe this logic and to set aside the truth that was glowing in my hand right before my eyes.

In the heat of the moment, I flippantly texted Tanner back and told him I was so disappointed in him and that he had completely embarrassed me. A few replies later and I still couldn't let it go. I continued to add salt to the wound and drag out the entire thing. I was even starting to annoy myself like *God Baleigh, he said sorry a million times; say it with me "Letitgo."* I couldn't just let this go of course. I was scared this was the beginning of the end, for real this time, and I was being so relentless and downright mean to drive the point home. I never wanted this to happen again because to me, it meant he was letting go. Letting go of me - of us. Out of fear, I scolded and guilted him until even I couldn't stand it any longer.

Eventually Tanner felt so terrible that he offered to drive the half hour out to Silvy's house just to apologize to her in person. I don't know where I got off making this man, who genuinely cared for me, feel like trash for something he did by accident. Twenty-four was not the best year for me personally. I was still remarkably unstable and had so much to learn yet about my anger, anxiety, and my feelings in general. The ones I loved the most always got the wrath of this, unfortunately. This was a prime example. I was watching in horror as the guilt trip poured from my mouth and rained abrasively down on Tanner, but I couldn't stop it. I knew it was wrong and incredibly unfair, but I let my fear take over my mouth and my mind.

I was overcorrecting the situation with Silvy and making it even worse. By the time the two of us made it back to her house, Silvy was over the whole situation entirely. "Baleigh, him driving out here now would be ridiculous, it's not that serious. It's fine. People fall asleep," she snapped at me. Then, like a scolded child, I was even more embarrassed. I fell silent then and followed her into the house where Emmy was waiting expectantly in her combat boots on the couch. I was grateful for Emmy's company breaking up the awkward silence that followed the end of Silvy and I's conversation.

Emmy and I quietly drank our beers while we let Silvy's annoyance simmer. With each bubbly sip I felt another tense muscle release. My mind was coming back to reality and my anger was circling the drain. Relaxing into the couch next to Emmy, my anger barely visible anymore, I decided to just enjoy this summer night with my friends. In the Midwest, it's a mutual understanding that warm nights are not to be taken for granted. Silvy, also seemingly calmed down and was now "over it", as the kids say. At about 10 p.m. she yawned and told us that she was heading to bed. I sensed that she was still a bit turned off by what had just transpired with Tanner and that she was ready for me to leave. Emmy and I exchanged a questioning look, shrugged our shoulders, and then collected our things to head out.

We tossed our goodbyes to a cold-mannered Silvy over our shoulders as we left and the second the door shut behind us, Emmy and I looked at each other devilishly. At the same time, we blurted out, "So the bars?" The "jinx" moment and sudden release of an hour-long tension between us and Silvy caused us to erupt into relieved laughter. Silvy could pout if she wanted to, but Emmy and I knew how to make the most of a warm summer night in Northeast Ohio.

It was obvious that we both knew it probably wasn't a good idea to start drinking so late but hey, I had gotten ditched, and my best friend was obviously annoyed with me, so why not just go and have a little fun? The night was still salvageable! Or at least that was what I was telling myself when we hopped into our cars and headed back downtown towards the college bars.

On the way there, I called Tanner to see if

he would want to come out with us now that he was so well-rested, and the drama had died down. It was late and a lot had just happened so I could tell he wasn't ready to meet Emmy after we'd both been drinking and talking about how Tanner had just messed up his first-time meeting Silvy. He quietly said that tonight was a wash for him and that he would like to wait until another weekend to try this again. I was mad in a juvenile and pouty way because I hadn't gotten my way twice now and worst of all, I still wasn't going to see Tanner. I couldn't let it go; I can never let anything go, so I said something catty like "fine good night" and threw my phone in my passenger seat.

Now that I had even more fuel added to my fire, there was no stopping me once we reached the overcrowded bars. Emmy and I did shots of tequila that we absolutely did not need, and we danced to songs we absolutely did not need to be dancing to. It was too much fun, really. I felt terribly old (hah! The naivety!) in the college bars and my tolerance seemed to match this old age that I was embodying. I mingled with girls that I knew would inevitably wake up with vomit in their hair the next morning and guys that would defeatedly watch while the vomiting happened.

The tequila was going down like water and before we knew it, 2 a.m. rolled around and it was time to go home. Emmy found a ride with some friends she met downtown, and I was going to wait for an Uber. I slurred to Emmy as we hugged goodbye "Text me when you're home!" and she slurred back, "You too!" I watched as her blonde spikey hair faded in the crowd and unlocked my phone to call my Uber. After I finally got my eyes to focus on the screen, I was horrified to see that it was going to be an hour long wait for a ride, at the earliest. My phone's battery life was at about 4% so that was not going to work. I had found myself in this situation before, so there was no panic creeping in. I always figured something out. That or I had a really overworked guardian angel. Probably the latter, I would assume.

I didn't want to call Emmy and make her friend come back and get me, so I tried calling Silvy. I knew she wouldn't answer because she was asleep, but I called anyway. I tried not to muster up some hope and found myself wandering away from the bars. I teetered toward the bridge that led to the gazebo above the river so I could collect my thoughts. I didn't even realize that my body was going where it felt safest: near the river. The river was Tanner to me now; it always would be.

I climbed down the stairs and sat on the bench that faced the river while I waited to see if Silvy would call back. She didn't. I watched the river flow along the rocks for a while before thinking of what to do next.

Now my battery was at 2% and I had to find a ride. Quickly. Sleeping on a park bench is a rock bottom that I had zero intention of hitting that night. I rapidly scrolled through my contacts until I found Tanner's name and I hovered over his name. I *really* didn't want to be the girl who fights with a guy and then drunkenly calls him the same night for a ride home, but I was running out of options. I finally punched the "call" button and instantly regretted it. I was mortified. At that moment I couldn't decide what would be worse: Tanner answering his phone or Tanner not answering his phone. I held my breath while the phone rang.

Saving my ass yet again, Tanner answered on the third ring and told me to stay where I was, he would be down to get me in a minute. I was embarrassed all over again but this time I had a tequila blanket that I could hide underneath to conceal my shame. I thanked him a million times and buried my head in my hands in shame. No matter what kind of trouble I get myself into, I always manage to find someone kind (or dumb?) enough to save my ass.

I counted the stars and looked for Mars while I waited for Tanner, it was an incredibly clear sky that night. My mind wandered as I began to get sleepy. I felt like I had only been sitting on that bench for 30 seconds when I heard Tanner's voice saying "Baleigh?" and I about jumped out of my skin. I didn't even hear him come down the steps, the man moved like a cat. I was suddenly so excited to see him (tequila always makes me a happy drunk) that I yelled "Tanner! You're here already! Come help me find Mars!" with an audible slur. He approached me as if I was a feral cat after hearing me slur and said "Okay, but then we have to go. It's almost 3 o'clock in the morning. Here, turn to the left a little bit, Mars is right there. See it?" I didn't see it, I couldn't really see much at that point honestly, but my sleepiness had already returned so I pretended to see it. I was getting dangerously close to passing out on that bench after all. I could feel my sleepy smile on my face, beaming up at Tanner. I was safe now that he was here; he would take care of me yet again. He was smiling at me too and I could only imagine it was because I had mascara smeared under my eyes and my hair was frizzing out of control from the humidity radiating off the river. Maybe he was just happy to be alone with me again; that did make him happy.

I started to head for Tanner's jeep that was parallel parked on the road when Tanner stopped me and said "Uh uh. We're taking your car. That way you won't have to find a way to get it in the morning." I tried to tell him he didn't have to do that and that he had already done more than enough, but he insisted. He said there would be an Uber available for him by the time we got back to my house, and he would just grab one back here to his Jeep. Between this act of kindness that I absolutely did not deserve and the tequila pulling at my emotions, I had to hold my breath so I wouldn't start to cry. Little things like making sure I had my car in the morning and letting my cousin wear his hoodie in a chilly movie theater made me more emotional than anything else. Simple things can go a long way and Tanner was the master of simple things. He turned my heart to honey, spilling between his fingers.

We climbed into my car and were berated by Bon Jovi blasting over the speakers. I had forgotten that I popped an old Bon Jovi album in right before parking the car earlier and had gotten a little carried away with "Born To Be My Baby" (I mean how do you not turn that song up as loud as you can when it comes on?) Tanner laughed and rolled his eyes at me as he turned it down. Nobody my age likes Bon Jovi, as Tanner loved to remind me, so I was used to this reaction. However, my tequila blanket of humility had slipped away, and I immediately started belting out the lyrics like no one else was in the car because tequila-Baleigh loves Bon Jovi even more than sober-Baleigh does, if that's possible.

Tanner was laughing and begging me to stop as I sang in a tone-deaf voice that only a mother could love so I finally gave in and joined him in laughing at me. I liked the way he was watching me sing. I knew it was bad, but he looked at me adoringly all the while laughing at my expense. He wanted me to stop but he was enjoying that I was being myself and showing him some vulnerability. I was just glad that he was at least enjoying himself on his pilgrimage to rescue me from myself. I turned the music down and thanked him again for doing this for me and he took my hand as he said "Oh it's my pleasure" like a sarcastic Chick-Fil-A employee.

We listened to a few more of Jon Bon Jovi's best hits and then we were rolling down my mom's street before we even got to my favorite song on the album, "Runaway". Tanner was spared this time.

Pulling into my driveway, Tanner flicked the headlights off while we waited for his Uber to arrive. The two of us passed the time by stargazing and giggling about one thing or another. Tanner slipped a pinch of chewing tobacco into his bottom lip as he often did to kill time. He tried not to do it around me because well, we kiss a lot, so he asked if I minded if he had a dip and I said no. Growing up in a little farm town where your high school had a two-page spread in the yearbook for "Drive-your-tractor-to-school Day" will make you feel all too comfortable being around chewing tobacco. It's one of those things that people are always "trying to quit" but usually never do. Tanner would fit in just fine in the military.

Once Tanner had situated his lip, I looked over to him and said "I'm sorry I got so upset with you tonight. I tend to be on edge around my loved ones. I feel so much pressure to impress them." He assured me that it was okay, saying it was "water under the bridge" with a wink. The wink melted me. I immediately slipped into the sappy side of drunk.

"Do you really have to leave me again?" I blurted out. Tanner's playful smirk dropped, and he leaned back in the seat as he said "Baleigh come on, don't do this right now. We've talked about this." I knew it wasn't the right time to bring it up, but it was the only thought that circulated my brain day in and day out.

"I'm sorry," I said, "I just. I just don't understand why God would put us together, have us create magic, and then tear us apart. There's got to be something more to it." Tanner looked so sad when I said this, but he was trying to be the strong one. The firm one.

"I know Baleigh, I know," he replied, "I'm so sorry. You know I am. This is my dream though, my future. I have to chase it, or I'll never forgive myself." Of course, I knew this too, but it didn't make his absence hurt any less. I dropped my head and stared at my pale fingers in my lap.

We moved onto lighter topics to ease the pain. We talked about the stars some more and joked about the hangover I would wake up with in the morning, and eventually a black sedan crept down the road and lingered by my mailbox; Tanner's Uber was here. The realization that it was time yet again for Tanner to leave my side sobered me up a bit and my heart ached. I hated this part. Tanner peered at the car through my rearview mirror and with a sigh he said "Well, that's my ride"

We got out of the car, despite my best efforts to not stumble, my toe caught the uneven pavement of our driveway and Tanner reached out instinctively to upright me. Cursing from the frustration at my legs' ineptness to do their ONE JOB, I hugged Tanner to cover up my clumsiness while we both laughed quietly at my faux pas.

With my face in his chest, I thanked him again for picking me up. He leaned back so he could look at my face to smile and say, "If you thank me one more time, I'm taking you back there." with a laugh. He knew he couldn't look at me like that without getting a kiss from me. I leaned my face closer to his and, jerking back, Tanner exclaimed, "Woah you don't want to kiss me!" while pointing to the bulge protruding from his bottom lip. My tequila-brain made my mouth respond with "Oh relax, you don't have to open your mouth!" and we both laughed at the rashness of my comment. Tanner shook his head as if to say, "Okay fine," and leaned down to give me what he knew I wanted. You know you've got it bad when you're willing to kiss a man with a mouthful Copenhagen.

I watched that little Honda whisk him away like a chariot and then headed inside to get ready for bed. I learned that night that Tanner wasn't perfect; he was human. It was jarring at first to realize he was capable of letting me down, but he had shown me something else that night too. While he could never be perfect, he would always be there when I needed him the most and he would never turn me away when I called. A man that oversleeps the day he is supposed to meet your best friend is not a man who is unworthy of a second chance. I condemned him too early and felt foolish now and he knew that. When he saw that I had gotten myself into potential danger, he swooped in to "save" me without hesitation, and I will never forget that.

While I washed my face and brushed my teeth that night, I felt the familiar sadness creep back in. It always picked me up where Tanner had set me down, to relentlessly remind me that Tanner's enlistment was another day closer now. I couldn't imagine how my night would have gone without Tanner and I didn't want to. That reality was hurtling towards me at the speed of light and before I could get a towel to my face, tears were streaming into the sink. I was sad that I had wasted one of our last days together fighting over something as trivial as a snoozed alarm. I wanted to redo the whole night, but I knew I would never get it back. Wiping the last tear from my face, I prayed to God. *Give me one more night with him please God. Don't let this be the night that he gives up on me completely. Not yet. I'm not ready. I will never be ready.*

11

The next morning, I could tell that every-thing had changed. Last night was a roller coaster of contradictory emotions. I could feel Tanner pulling away yet again because he knew he had to get his mind right and his wits about him before making the big decision to en-list. That night was the last night that was about us. From here on out it would be about Tanner and his career. There was no more room for our love that tended to suck the air out of the room like a vacuum.

The following weeks passed slowly, and I felt the air around me begin to grow stale and uncom-fortable without the vying eyes of Tanner on my face. Tanner was replying less and less to my text messages, and it was like pulling teeth to get him to go on a river walk anymore. He started working out twice a day and researching to prepare for his bon voyage to the Navy. When he wasn't working, he was at the gym, the pool, or briefly sleeping. Not only was he physically unavailable, but he also became more and more secluded mentally; lost in his own plans. When we were together, he wasn't present anymore. Our conversations turned from my fears and his dreams to recruiters and paperwork. The clenching of his jaw and his distracted eyes that flicked to the horizon when I spoke were enough to send me to the brink of tears on most days; I was already losing him. He was standing right next to me but mentally, he was no longer in Kent, Ohio with me; he was already at boot camp in Illinois or out in the deserts of the middle east.

While texting with me one day, Tanner mentioned that his cousin was a Navy SEAL that lived in Hawaii with his wife and Tanner was leaving soon to visit him for a week. The plan was to get a crash course on all things SEAL training and have his cousin whip him into shape. This would be the kiss of death that sealed (no pun intended) his fate with the Navy. A mentor that he adored like a superhero was going to show him the ropes of his dream job. What little space I still took up in Tanner's heart would be taken from me and placed in the ripping currents of the Pacific Ocean.

I was taking more walks along the river by myself in those long days. I lounged in the vine swing and listened to music on our rock wall all the while reaching for his absent hand in the breeze. Tanner had mentioned briefly on one of our walks that I should start writing again to ease my anxiety when it gets too heavy to carry so I took his advice.

From the comfort of the vine swing I wrote about all the weights that were holding my heart to the ground on any given day. I wrote until my hand was cramped sometimes. Other times I wrote short letters to Tanner that I would never send him. In my letters I thanked him for bringing me back to life and I chastised him for leaving me to write alone on a swing that he once shared with me. I would beg, curse, and love like only a woman can in those letters. I left nothing out and I didn't bother to hide my ugly resentment that I could no longer keep covered up. That's one way to get back to writing I suppose. It was the only form of therapy that didn't come with a hefty price tag, and I ran with it.

My anxiety lay dormant in my chest and my notebooks during these lonely weeks. Distraction will do that. I didn't have time for anxiety because I was too busy thinking up new ways to get Tanner to acknowledge me. Panic took the backseat to my desperation for his time. Fighting off the looming heartbreak that was floating just off the coast of my summer consumed my every thought and action. I couldn't accept that I might one day forget what color Tanner's eyes were, so I shut my brain off entirely. I lived in an ignorant cloud of bliss for as long as I could.

I could feel the end coming with the changing winds of autumn, but I wasn't ready yet. I still needed those late nights and his crazy stories.

I needed to hear his laugh reverberating off the cement walls of the tunnel that reminded me of the movie *IT*. I needed more of his pocket-smiles.

After he told me of his plans for Hawaii, I was again asking (begging) Tanner for a walk one day before he left. He was taking a while to respond; longer than usual. Hours and hours had passed without a response from him. This new lax way of responding had become the norm now that Tanner's mind was elsewhere. Yet again I found myself taking the river walk alone. This one lasted long after dark just in case Tanner showed up at the last minute.

Just as I was trudging up the slight hill to where my car was parked, I finally heard from him. I assumed he was going to apologize for falling asleep after work again or getting caught up swimming laps at the rec center, but his tone was different now. It was more flippant and distracted like he was desperately trying to wedge us further apart. I knew something was up, so I asked him what was wrong. Leaning against my car for support, I read his gutting reply. Tanner hadn't dozed off or lost track of time at the gym this time-he was leaving me. Again. It read:

"I'm sorry Baleigh, but like I said before, there's nothing wrong with you and I like everything about you, but it is me who has issues, and I don't have time for a relationship. That's not fair to you and I don't wanna drag you along. You deserve someone who can put more into this, and I don't think that person is me. We should stop seeing each other. If we can remain friends that's great but I understand things don't always work that easily. If you ever need anything don't hesitate to ask, I will always do what I can for you."

My body folded in on itself slowly as his words seeped in through the shock. I was gutted by the sudden blow and rendered useless. I couldn't breathe, and tears were coming in sheets. Blinded by my despair, all I could think was "*He promised.*"

He promised that last time would be the only time he ever tried to leave me. I was there, laying with my head on his chest while Brandi Carlile's album drifted in and out of our whispered conversation in his giant bed, when he promised he wouldn't do this again. *How could he go back on his word and do this to me again? Didn't he know that would destroy me? Did he no longer care?* These questions hammered through my brain one after another faster than I could keep up with. It was overwhelming to be this hurt all at once. I was lost.

All the colors that Tanner had introduced to me faded to their original dull form. Like placing an airtight lid on the flame of a candle, the light that he had lit inside me was quickly extinguished. I was watching it all happen, my knees buckling, the tears streaming down, and my hands shaking from an out of body vantage point. Being stuck on pause while your body is still in motion is a battle, and I wasn't winning this one. The immediate pain of realizing this new love I had so deeply believed in was ending, washed over me like the shadow of a passing cloud.

I had felt so much despair in the last couple of years, from losing friends, to those three long days spent in the behavioral health hospital, that I thought I had felt the worst of the worst pain. I thought I could never hurt like that again but here I was face-to-face with it. The same gnawing burn in the pit of my stomach that haunted me for months was back like it had never left. I remembered this feeling all too well. It was the agony of losing a part of myself that I loved dearly. If I shut my eyes, I was back in that rubber cot or the folding chair in the funeral home three rows away from my friend's lifeless body, surrounded by my classmates. Not having Tanner in my life anymore would mean that I would have to grieve again, and grieving takes so much from my heart that sometimes I can't find my way back out of it.

This wasn't just "being dumped" - it was losing my new favorite part of myself. The person I was when I was with Tanner was my favorite person to be; he had reawakened my heart and my happiness and I had no idea how to keep it alive without him. Tanner's personality and pure heart had introduced a sense of peace that my soul had never been able to find elsewhere, and it was terrifying to think of losing that now. I liked that I wasn't so afraid of everything when he was near. I liked that I didn't have to filter my thoughts before giving them to him to digest. He got me to start writing again, to open my mind, and to refocus on love in the sense of only doing things out of love rather than hate or anger. All this beauty we had been making together was going to be cut short now and I had to find a way to accept that.

I don't remember what I messaged back to him or if I even replied at all. All I remember is finding my way to my bed where I could fall apart with the safety of knowing that my mattress would catch all my pieces before they hit the floor.

I cried in the dark for three hours before I could finally tell Silvy what had happened. She tried her damnedest to comfort me, as she always did, but this was an ache that could not be soothed by her careful words this time. After popping melatonin to stop the tears just long enough to be pulled to sleep, I realized that falling asleep was only half the battle. I kept waking up and ripping the scab off my heart all over again. I would fall asleep for a couple hours and then, without fail, my eyes would spring open again. Then I would start the whole process over again. I cried a deep, primal cry that racked my lungs against my ribs, and I couldn't make it stop. I realized I wasn't just sad; I was mourning Tanner, and this was how my body mourned.

I stayed in bed for three days, weighed down

with my grief; sometimes crying, sometimes trying to figure out how to move on, and neither option being preferable over the other. I don't remember if I told my mom what happened or if she just figured it out. I knew she was worried, but I was so broken that I couldn't even muster the energy to appease her with an embellished illness.

By the end of day three, Silvy had grown worried too. She reached out to me with one final plea of, "Okay. No more. We're going for a walk. You need to eat, and you need some sun. If you're not by the river in a half hour, I'm breaking into your mom's house and dragging you out of bed."

Last time I had gone through a breakup, Silvy took me to a park where you could take a paddle boat out into alligator-infested waters; except she didn't tell me there were alligators in the pond until we were already paddling our way across it. She claimed it was just to make me feel alive again and take my mind off the breakup, but we freaked ourselves out so badly that we almost immediately turned around to flee to dry land. Remembering those alligators was the only thing that got me out of bed. I knew if I didn't get up now, Silvy would do something - anything - to get me out of the house so it was better to leave on my own recognizance than face the consequences. Silvy had spent a lot of her life grieving, so she knew the process well unfortunately. She knew when to let a person disappear and when to real them back into reality before they were lost to their grief forever. Hence the alligators.

Dragging my deflated body from my dirty sheets felt like trying to clap underwater; I was exerting the required amount of effort, yet the action was still happening in slow motion. Getting myself dressed took the same amount of momentous effort and I wondered just how long I had been lying dormant under my covers after all. According to my body, it had been years. Judging by the sunlight peeking around the edges of my dark curtains, it was another hot day in late July. I pulled on some shorts and a tank top, threw my hair up in a bun, and made the slow dissent downstairs towards my running shoes. The sunlight that was beaming in through the windows in the foyer hurt my eyes and I squinted to look for my keys. When I walked through the garage door and out into the thick summer air, I felt like I had been in a coma for years. I was so tired, and my legs felt atrophied from missing a few days of long walks along the river. I wished my heart was capable of being as forgetful as my leg muscles.

Silvy was waiting for me in the parking lot of the hike-and-bike trail with a welcoming smile on her face and her blonde hair in a jaunty ponytail. She knew what I was going through; her and her mother were empaths through and through and they absorbed their loved one's pain into their own bodies like heat. She hugged me and asked how I was doing. I told her that everything hurt, and I was so, so tired. She told me I looked like hell to make me laugh but it would've been funnier if it wasn't so glaringly true. My greasy hair was stuck to my head in sloppy patterns, my stomach was caved in, my skin was ghostly pale, and my clothes didn't even *kind of* match. I told her to be happy that I had at least brushed my teeth for her. Silvy looked at me like I was pathetic, and I was. I was pathetic. I didn't know how to heal this wound without Tanner. She promised to get me through this, and we began our stroll along the river as my attention caught on the word "promise."

In the sobering light of day, I realized it was time to decide. I couldn't live the rest of my life like this so I had to decide if I could just be friends with Tanner or if I had to expel him from my life entirely. Silvy and I talked about the pros and cons until we decided that I was better off with Tanner in my life, even if only in the most miniscule way. It didn't sit right with me to only think of Tanner as a friend. He was so much more than that to me and I knew from the second that I met him that he always would be. But I had to do this if I wanted to keep our bridge from completely burning to the ground.

I opened a blank text message and with my teeth grinding together, typed out my message to Tanner explaining we could remain friends. We both obviously still wanted to be in each other's lives so there was no sense in cutting him out entirely. While I knew this was just slapping a band aid on a bullet wound, it was all I had left. There were no more options. He was happy to hear my decision so that was how we ended the conversation.

Still, the trees didn't seem to be as vibrant anymore; their bright greens and neutral browns fading with my sense of hope. In a childish way I believed, until now, that Tanner and I would still somehow make it. We would make it, in a Hallmark movie kind of way. I believed that a love as intense as this one could never be struck down by the throws of reality. I loved Tanner enough to wait the rest of my life for him and he cared for me so much that he would never let me do that. And with that, my fate was sealed. I had to let go of my romantic love for Tanner and embrace this new unconditional love that sets no geographical limits or time constraints. I had to let him go and hold onto my blind faith that the universe knew what it was doing. I leaned into my decision and put my heart back in God's hands; he was kinder to it than I had ever been anyway.

The following week Tanner left for Hawaii, and I continued writing again to pass the time. He sent me pictures of the beautiful waterfalls and the ocean, followed by a video from a reggae concert he and his cousin attended to fill the void of our actual feelings. Our conversations as friends were quick and menial to avoid any emotions sneaking into this new "friendship." I hated this, but I knew we were trying our best to tiptoe around our hearts that were lying on the ground at our feet. I told him that I was happy and excited for him, but what I didn't tell him was that I felt lost back home without him here. Nor did I tell him that now the energy along the river felt emptier knowing that he wasn't close by. I never really believed in sensing another person's energy until meeting Tanner. When he was near, the air on the path felt singed with the sparks of electricity and energy coursing through it. However, when he was gone, the air was calm and lifeless as snow. It was a foreign feeling, being so attuned to another person's energy that you could sense if they were near or not.

As the nights dragged on, Tanner stopped replying to me entirely. There was nothing left to say, nothing real anyway. I suppose this was to be expected at this point in our slow transition from friends to acquaintances and eventually, strangers. To keep me occupied, Silvy and Emmy spent their afternoons walking the trails, going to Indians games, and drinking beers at a new ledge I had stumbled upon that was even closer to the river, with me. I pretended that peering from a new ledge and laughing with people that weren't Tanner along our river was freeing but inside, my stomach rolled. It didn't feel right. The river flowed just inches from my feet, but I couldn't hear its tinkling babble. I glanced up towards the walking path with every snap of a twig for Tanner's bike. I felt so out of place being there without him, like a puzzle piece that appeared to fit to the naked eye but upon closer inspection it was glaringly obvious that it was the wrong shape. I didn't belong at this river without Tanner. It was the dreamland that we had created for ourselves; how could I ever feel at home here with anyone other than him?

I was considering this one muggy afternoon on the ledge with the girls when Tanner's name flashed across my phone screen. It had been about a week since I last heard from Tanner, and Silvy and I locked eyes immediately. Her expression was questioning, and I could see that mine, reflecting off her glossy eyes, was terrified. I took another big gulp of my Blue Moon and opened the message while Silvy leaned in to read along with me. It asked, simply, "Are you down by the river?" and my blood ran cold. This time, Silvy's shocked expression matched my own as we gaped at each other. *Was he here? I thought he was in Hawaii? Could he see me right now?* I wondered to myself. Reading my mind, Silvy sternly said to me "Do not reply to him." This was the smart choice, but I couldn't help myself and I replied that I was by the river (this was the not-smart choice), but that I was with my friends. I followed that message with, "I thought you were in Hawaii?"

Tanner had come home early and apparently, had seen my car parked in the lot while riding his bike down the path. I told him that we could go for a walk tomorrow, but I didn't tell Silvy that part, I wanted her to be proud of me a little bit longer, so I told her I ditched him. I knew she could tell I was distracted the rest of the night and I didn't care to hide it. It felt like it had been forever since I had seen Tanner and I was nervous things would be awkward now. My skin itched at the thought of being near him again so soon. Goosebumps sprouted up all over my body and my legs began to tremble. I hoped that he wouldn't treat me any differently and that his hand would disregard his words and reach for mine like it used to.

The next night slowly arrived, and I was sure to get to the hike-and-bike trail an hour before Tanner and I were supposed to meet. I needed to fit a long walk into the mix to calm my nerves and center my thoughts. I went back to my new ledge and told Tanner he could meet me there. I sent him a picture of my surroundings and he knew exactly where the spot was, of course. He knew that entire park like the back of his hand.

I heard the spokes of his bike plucking along the brick path from where I was perched on the mossy boulders, and I stiffened as I waited to hear footsteps approaching through the weeds. I looked up just as he was closing in on my hiding spot and we smiled timidly at each other in recognition. His hair was shorter, his skin tanner, and his arms seemed to be more solid in his black tank top now. I was quiet as he sat next to me and then we encountered the first awkward silence between the two of us as we watched the river flow beneath our feet.

I broke the silence by asking him how his trip went. I couldn't believe out of all the important words that were berating the backs of my teeth, I had chosen small talk. He beamed as he showed me more pictures and videos of the powerful ocean waves he had swam through with his cousin. I was pleased to see him so excited, he seemed to confidently know what he wanted to do with his life now and I loved that for him. There was still a sense of apprehension when he talked about shipping out, but I would be more worried if he wasn't nervous to go on this crazy journey alone.

Another awkward silence settled over us like a dense fog. I couldn't hold back any longer, and I whispered, "I missed you." He lifted his head and pierced me with his eyes as he hesitantly replied, not wanting to get my hopes up, "I missed you too, Baleigh." I knew he meant it and the tear in my heart ripped even deeper. I wondered if he could hear it. Not having the ability to say anything else and not having the mental capacity to decide what else could even be said, I decided not to say anything and just sit in the moment with Tanner.

By that time at night, the peepers were singing their guttural summer songs and the mosquitos were eating us alive. We were both cumbersome from the sad realization that there was nothing more we could say to one another, so we began the long walk back to our cars. We fell into lighter conversation on the way back and I realized I was laughing with him again. He was teasing me by regaling me with a dramatic rendition of how well he slept on the long flight home that would have put me into a panic-induced coma. At one point he had his head thrown back and was fake snoring to accent this story. He peaked one eye open to see if I was glaring at him and then, upon seeing that I was, began to laugh his genuine laugh at his own joke. I laughed with him and told him to shut up as I took a mental picture of Tanner's smile like Jim did of Pam in the episode of The Office where they finally get married. Now when I spent time with Tanner, I was constantly aware that this may be the last time for a very long time, so I took a million mental pictures just like that one. I prayed they would never be faded by the unforgiving hands of time. *Click*

The two of us were yawning by the time we reached the parking lot; it had to have been almost 10 o'clock at night. I leaned into Tanner to hug him goodbye, and he reciprocated with his own embrace. I lingered in his arms and held my breath to try and not let the tears tip over the brim of my eyelids. It just wasn't fair. I didn't understand why God had given me this man only to take him away as soon as I had embedded him in my heart. I slowly let my breath out, desperately trying to make the moment last longer, and recoiled as I felt Tanner begin to pull away. The moment was over as quickly as it had begun, leaving my body cold where he had just been. We got into our cars, and I looked in my rearview mirror as his taillights turned right onto Summit Road. It wasn't until I was the last car in the parking lot that I finally allowed my tears to drench my face and rain down onto my T-shirt. I missed him terribly already.

I had no idea how I was going to get through this, but I knew I had no other option. Having even just a shred of Tanner in my life was better than nothing at all - at least I was out of bed now. I knew it was time now to take Tanner off the top shelf and move him to a lower one with all my other dreams of what could have been. I hoped that he would save part of himself for me, but I understood if he couldn't. This wasn't any easier for him than it was for me, or at least that was what I was telling myself, and we were both dealing with it in our own way. I prayed that ten years from now I would be driving past the river with nothing but fond memories, but I couldn't ignore the nagging feeling that as I drove by the river, ten years older, that I would be thinking *I wonder if he still misses me too.* I told myself that time would heal this wound, and Tanner and I would settle comfortably into a lasting friendship soon enough. God laughed at this insight, as he often does, when we plan our own destinies.

12

July faded into August, and it was taking everything I had not to ask Tanner to go for a walk with me every single day like a sad old woman. It was just so unbearably lonesome to go alone when I knew how full this place had once made my heart feel before. Tanner rarely replied to my propositions, and I felt myself sinking lower and lower into my depressed state of mind. On one particularly low day, I texted Tanner and asked him if he thought love was real because I was starting to question the validity of it. Something as real as the love I had for him should be the end of my story; Tanner and I should ride off into the sunset and live happily ever after. My love for him was what I had always dreamt of, and it fit me like a second skin so the fact that he would be leaving, and we wouldn't be together, destroyed every notion of love that I had ever had. If this love, this man, wasn't meant for me, then "love" and what it meant to me was unattainable.

I know I said there's a lid for every pot and that Tanner was my lid, but what if he wasn't? I don't want the leftover, dented, and rusted lids that previous owners have used and abused beyond recognition. I want the lid that was specifically made for me, and I had thought that lid was Tanner. He was so much so my "lid" in my mind that I was questioning the other lids I had tried on in the past. I questioned whether that love had been real, or if I had just doctored it up in mind. I had loved other men, but nothing compared to what I was feeling now. Tanner was the blissful ignorance you have as a child regarding life-untouchable, death-defying, hundreds of millions of days ahead of you without an end in sight. You woke up every day and did whatever the hell you wanted to do and ate whatever you wanted to eat because danger and fear didn't exist yet. When Tanner had his arms around me, danger no longer existed. He was peace. He was home. My home.

When I asked Tanner if he believed in love he said:

"This is a tough conversation for texting. Love is different for everyone. It's definitely real and everything you grew up reading, watching and learning about has really happened in someone's life. Thinking back on past experiences is difficult because you're not the same person that you were then [in those previous relationships]. You have lived and learned a lot since those times. Love is real. It does last. Troubles aside, those experiences have stuck with you for a reason. You can't give up on love. Yeah, unfortunately, some never find it nor even experience it because it is just that, rare. You're very young, and still have a very long life to live. You can't necessarily search for it; I think the best kind of love always catches people off guard. It's okay to think about it and dream of it but just keep living a good life and it'll find you along the way. Don't give up on love, it's very real."

By the time I reached the last sentence of his text, I was bawling my eyes out for all the wrong reasons. Instead of taking in his earnest message objectively, I took it as Tanner telling me that just because my love for him was not going to work out, that I shouldn't give up on finding love elsewhere. I hated that he was confirming that I needed to move on. It broke so many different parts of me to absorb this presumed realization.

It took me some time to experience his words for what they were: hope. Tanner cared so much for me that he wanted me to live the best life that I could ever possibly dream of, even if he couldn't be a part of it. He knew that I deserved to be loved fully and entirely, he just couldn't be the man to give that to me. I wish for my younger self, that she would have appreciated the weight of his message for all that it was. *Baleigh you idiot, he wasn't throwing you away, he cared so much for you that he wanted you to experience true happiness.*

I messaged Tanner again agreeing that this was a difficult discussion for texting and that we were long overdue for a walk. We landed on a day that we were both available after work to catch up with a hike along our river. I was excited to see Tanner, of course, but also feeling indifferent at the same time. Every time we saw each other anymore I had a hard time trusting it wasn't for the last time. Tanner was a flight-risk now and I had to cherish all the time I could pull from him because I knew that soon, he would be gone.

The long days at work and even longer nights out with Silvy and Emmy passed slowly as I waited for the day of Tanner and I's rendezvous. After an excruciatingly long day in the sweatshop that I called work, it was time to head home and change into new clothes for our walk. As usual, I didn't bother with makeup, threw my long heavy hair on top of my head into a makeshift bun and shoved my feet into my sneakers without untying the laces first. I messaged Tanner letting him know that I was on my way and surprisingly, he texted back immediately with "be there in one minute." His quick response brought me back to a time not so long ago when Tanner would be excited to go for a walk with me again. I longed for those days now, but I refused to let myself think anything more of his promptness. I knew it would be a fleeting thing.

Pulling into my usual parking spot in the park, I dug my phone out of my purse to let Tanner know that I had arrived. Before I could even punch the passcode in, I saw in my rearview mirror that he was leaning against his jeep, already waiting for me to get out of my car. I threw the gearshift in park and cut the ignition before stepping out into the harsh sunlight. Laughing, I said to Tanner, "You know how creepy it was to look in my rearview mirror and see you standing behind my car, just staring at me?" and he laughed at his realization of his Edward Cullen move.

It felt so good to see his smile again, pulling ever so slightly to the left as always. Taking my time basking in his grin, I decided that this new-found lightness in Tanner must mean that his enlistment process was moving along nicely. Before I could ask him how it was going, he was leading me down the trail toward the river while regaling me with a summary of the most recent Joe Rogan podcast episode. For a minute, everything was the way it was supposed to be again. Like nothing had changed. Like I was still in that carefree world with Tanner before reality got in the way and forced us to set our hearts aside.

Tanner may not have been mine but if we could still have these little talks beside the river, I suppose that wasn't so bad. I could still love him from behind the cover of the willow trees for now.

Allowing myself the peace that came with these lighter conversations with Tanner, I told him all about the tattoo I was planning to have done soon. I had a dozen or so tattoos at this point, and

I was finally starting to dabble in the more visible areas of my body. This one was going right smack dab on the top of my left arm, starting at my shoulder and stretching all the way to my elbow. I've always adored my tattoos and the little meanings behind them. I started collecting them at the age of 18 and I was hooked immediately.

Since this tattoo was going to be my most visible one, it was important that it was beautiful and meaningful and spoke to who I truly am. Tanner knew of my adoration for the Bon Jovi song, "Wildflower" so I knew he would love the idea like I did. I was going to have a wildflower drawn up with splashes of watercolor reds, pinks, deep greens and browns across the outside of my arm. Then, running horizontally down my bicep, the words "She's at home with the weeds" from my favorite lyric of that song.

When I first heard this song at the ripe young age of thirteen, it resonated so deeply in my soul, but I couldn't quite understand why. Probably because I was still a child. As I grew older, however, I realized why the lyrics hit home; I saw myself to be very unremarkable to look at but wildly intuitive. The "roses" were the prom queens and bombshells of my high school, college, and even work peers. They slathered on their lipstick and kissed all the beautiful boys while I spent my summers playing softball and my lunch periods reading books. I was the wildflower on the side of the road, perfectly at home with the weeds that grew on either side of me.

Tanner's eyes lit up as he exclaimed how much he adored the tattoo idea and couldn't wait to see it when it was done. I loved the fact that he was just as thrilled with the concept as I was because he truly understood the meaning of the lyrics and what they meant to me. We walked and talked about everyday things like tattoos and podcasts for about a mile before the military reared its dominating head into our easy conversation.

The air had grown pregnant with the words we didn't want to say, and it closed in on our moment of simplicity. Tanner sucked in a deep inhale as he finally spit out that he would be signing his contract with the Navy soon, like in a month soon. His sobering statement brought me back to reality and the lingering sadness in my blood began to flow freely again through my veins. I pretended to be excited for Tanner as he told me he would start training soon for bootcamp. It was all becoming real now, and he was getting closer to witnessing his dreams come true.

Suddenly, I remembered his text message about not giving up on love and I was unable to hide the pain on my face. Tanner's expression mirrored mine after he noticed the shift in my mood, and he asked me "Are you okay?" Instead of answering his question honestly, I childishly dodged his and asked my own, "I just want to swing for a bit. Do you know where we could do that?" Pretending not to notice my redirection of the conversation, Tanner said, "Of course I do, there's a park with swings just up that gravel path past the gazebo."

We began the steep hike up the slightly hidden gravel path and I found myself wondering how I had never thought to see where this path led before. We had passed by it at least a dozen times this summer but it never occurred to me to explore its route. Reaching the peak of the gravel path, I was surprised to see a sprawling park with at least three different playground areas all adorned with matching sets of swings. There were three different parking areas, lots of winding hills, and large pavilions lining the beaten paths that encompassed the park. Tanner picked a smaller set of swings that only had the occupancy for two people at a time so we could maintain our privacy.

I squished my butt into a swing that was clearly made for a child and began to pump my legs in the air instinctively. Tanner sat in the swing next to me and mimicked my childlike leg-pumping as we swung in unison for a while, not saying a word. Finally, lifting the veil of remorse that had fallen over me earlier, I asked Tanner if he was scared to ship out. He smiled and looked to the ground as he said "Hell yeah I am. This is going to be the hardest thing I have ever done and I'm starting to shit my pants a little bit now," with a gentle laugh.

I was glad he was being honest with me about his anxiety about leaving, but I knew he would have no problem completing the training; he was so smart and incredibly devoted to things he felt strongly about. With a genuine smile, I told him I had full confidence that he would do just fine, and he replied with a cautious "I hope you're right."

He talked to me for a while about not only the physical hardships he would have to endure, but also the mental torment that recruits go through during SEAL training. Tanner was meditating twice a day to strengthen his ability to remain mentally resilient during times of distress, but he was nervous that this wouldn't be enough. To an outsider of Tanner's mind, it would be easy to feel confident that he would complete the training with ease. However, I was not an outsider to Tanner's mind, and I knew just how sensitive he could be in comparison to most military members. From what I learned about the military via my ex-boyfriend, recruits with big hearts don't last long in the race toward a uniform and Tanner had one of the biggest hearts I'd ever had the pleasure of knowing. While he was very strong-willed, he was also very in tune with his emotions and catered to them immensely, sometimes even subconsciously. However, I couldn't help but think that if he could push me aside like he had, then he could also push any emotion aside to protect himself too.

Seeing his hesitation, I asked him again if this was what he really wanted and without missing a beat he said he knew this was something he was meant to do; he felt called to do it. I mentally noted that this did not answer the question I had asked. Feeling like you have to do something and wanting to do something were two totally different things, but I let it go because he was absently writing his initials in the sand under our feet with a stick as he told me this. It was such an endearing act of vulnerability and fear that I was glad he didn't realize he was doing it. It was a private moment that I got to look in on from the outside. I knew at that moment he needed support and that was what I was going to give him, whether I fully meant it or not. Adjusting the rusty chains of my swing, I told him I supported his choice. I also told him I hoped he would find, if nothing else, a sense of purpose and pride in the Navy. He deserved to have that, and so much more.

Being that I have the body of a 60-year-old woman, my hips didn't last too long in those tiny swings and my legs were beginning to go numb. Staggering to my feet, I told Tanner I had to walk around some more or he would have to carry me back to my car soon. Laughing at my premature geriatric aches and pains, Tanner led me back down the gravel path towards the river yet again. As the sweet sounds of the river grew closer, Tanner shocked me by asking "So what was that text about earlier? About not believing in love anymore?" and I felt my face flush with embarrassment. I didn't think we would talk about this in person to be honest, the issue felt resolved after reading Tanner's response. Shuffling my feet, I responded "I don't know. Just a bad day for me I suppose. Love seems to become less attainable with each year of my life that passes."

See, I did this often. I started a statement flippantly and then tapered it off with a large, heavy talking point that I had been carrying in my pocket for years but was never brave enough to say aloud. Tanner looked at me with a hint of sadness as he said, "Love Isn't unattainable for you, you're just trying too hard to make it happen." and I knew he was right. Love was the golden oil lamp buried deep within the cave of wonders that no matter how many times I entered, it would inevitably collapse over me before I could meet the magical genie. I wanted it so badly that I had turned it into a myth; something many people talked about but only a few had seen. You had to be a special person, hand-picked by God, to receive a true and honest love that was yours to keep for the rest of your life. But as history shows, love is given to roses, not wildflowers.

Pushing the envelope, I added "It's not even just romantic love. I couldn't even keep my own father in my life and he's one of the few people that was supposed to be a guaranteed everlasting love. If my father couldn't love me, how can I expect a perfect stranger to?"

Saying it out loud, I knew this wasn't how I truly felt; I was just feeling sorry for myself. I had been loved deeply by so many perfect strangers in this life. I knew my statement held no morsel of truth, but it was still a thought that had clung to my consciousness ever since I could remember, and it felt so weird to air it out now.

Tanner frowned in response and his face contorted into a perplexed expression. It was as if he was deciding how he wanted to express his response to me. Finally, as if deciding to just go for it, he said "I'm going to say something, and I don't want you to take it negatively at all because that's not my intention."

I nodded tentatively, letting him know it was okay to tell me how he felt. Slowing his pace, Tanner said, "What you just said is an incredibly narcissistic way to view that situation." Stunned by the harshness of his words, my jaw dropped, and my heart began to race in anticipatory anger. *How dare he?* He held his hands up to cut me off before I could refute his clam. "Before you get upset, let me explain what I mean by that. Thinking that your father's inability to love you is your fault is narcissistic in that it really has nothing to do with you or who you are. There was something incredibly wrong with your father, not you, and that's on him and him alone."

I snapped my mouth shut as the warmth of his words melted the anger from my rigid body. Realizing that I was unable to verbally respond yet, Tanner continued, "Working on being more positive and less pessimistic would do wonders for your outlook on love. I feel like you may spend so much time reveling in the ugly parts of love that you forget how beautiful it can be. Here, come sit down here with me for a minute."

Still at a loss for words, I followed Tanner in silence down the cement ravine that led to the boulders in the river we had sat on months ago. I sat on the slab of rock I had previously rested on and to my dismay, Tanner sat on his own rock next to mine rather than sharing a rock with me. I knew there was a lesson or something upsetting approaching by the stiffness in his posture. Pointing to a sagging weeping willow that was dipping lightly into the surface of the river, Tanner asked me: "When you look at that weeping willow, what do you see?" Wanting to be as honest as I could, I answered "I see a sad tree sagging into the water. The arch in its trunk makes her look tired and sad, like she's dying maybe." Tanner stared at me with his mouth pursed in a tight line, as if he was disappointed in me. This was a look I had never seen him give me and I hated how it felt. Finally, he said, "Do you want to know what I saw when I looked at that tree?" Feeling like this was a trick question, I nodded my head slowing up and down.

"When I saw that willow tree leaning down toward the river I thought 'that tree loves the river, just like you and I do'. The water is a life source to the tree so naturally she would lean her branches towards it in her gratitude. She exudes love and just wants to be near the water."

I was so taken aback by his perspective of the tree that all I could do was scoff at the stark differences in how we viewed the world. In that moment, I decided I would make more of an effort to view the world as that weeping willow tree. I didn't want to be sad anymore, I wanted to enjoy the world like Tanner did. I couldn't believe that I had spent 24 years of my life seeking sadness in otherwise beautiful things. After this realization I began mentally replaying my life in bite-size moments and combing through the sad strands to see what I had missed. I could've met my father, I could've walked across the stage to receive my college diploma in North Carolina instead of being holed up in that behavioral health hospital, and I could've rejoiced in Tanner's steps towards finding himself like I was now doing for myself, but I didn't. I let my fear, negativity, and anxiety ruin all those things for me. I don't think I spoke another word aloud to Tanner for at least ten minutes, gripped by my epiphany and mourning my missed opportunities that my negativity and fear stole from me.

Understanding that I needed to take some time to myself to sit with this new revelation, Tanner said "Maybe we should head home? Today was heavy and I think we're both exhausted." and I nodded my head again, still unable to find words that complemented what I was feeling inside. We walked the short distance back to our cars almost entirely in silence. I could tell Tanner was nervous that he had hurt me more than he had helped me. He hugged me just a bit too long, like he was trying desperately to put me back together. I hugged him back, gave my best "I'm fine" smile and then turned on my heel to get back into my car. I couldn't bear to look behind me at Tanner as he backed out of the parking lot and made his way up the street to the main intersection. I knew my smile had not fooled him and that he would feel guilty for upsetting me. Once I clipped my seatbelt on and made sure Tanner was long gone, and I could no longer hold it in, my heart exploded all over my steering wheel yet again.

I sobbed and sobbed until I couldn't catch my breath. I didn't even know why I was crying but I'm sure I was mourning how much of my life I wouldn't be able to get back or redo with a vision of positivity surrounding it. I was feeling regretful and rarely did I allow myself to feel this way. I couldn't help but wonder if my pessimistic tendencies were what landed me in the mental health hospital rather than my chemical imbalances - and that was a scary thought. Realizing you have control over the bad things in your life is scary because that means it's up to you then, to make them go away. While I knew it truly was a mental disorder, I wondered what hand my inability to accept happiness played in me being admitted. I hated this feeling, and I hated that Tanner felt bad for me now. I didn't want him to pity me or see me as a weak woman. Appearing to be strong was something I took seriously because there was nothing worse than allowing a man to feel he was stronger than me. That gives them control, and with an anxiety disorder comes the need for control in all aspects of life.

I wanted so badly to go back to June; back to dodging in between raindrops with Tanner laughing next to me, stopping only to kiss again. I hated that I couldn't seem to leave this parking lot without first soaking my face in tears.

I opened my phone after finally catching my breath and texted Tanner: "I can't stop crying. I just feel so unsure of everything in the entire world now. I hate this." Three little dots appeared immediately, meaning that Tanner was already typing his reply:

"Just breathe...everything is fine. You know who you are and what you need to do."

For once though, I knew Tanner was wrong. So wrong. I had no idea what to do now. I felt like I was free falling and blindly grasping for anything that may catch me and to no avail. With confusion also comes anger, at least for me. I was irrationally overcome with anger towards Tanner. How dare he do this to me and then just leave me to figure it out on my own with no further guidance? He knew I was vulnerable and in a weird place in my life and yet he left me grappling. I fired back a text saying: "Why do you keep doing this to me? You build me up just to tear me down and then watch from a distance as I crumble. You're killing me Tanner, seriously." without giving myself time to think it over before hitting send.

Not surprisingly, Tanner didn't respond. I knew it wasn't fair of me to pin my fear and confusion on him and blame him for all the guilt I was feeling, but it was easier to displace my uncomfortable feelings than to sit with them.

It was around this time that I decided it was time to start seeing a therapist again. I hated having to crawl back to 'Have-you-tried-breathing?" Margie but the comfort of familiarity overthrew my pride. I knew I wanted to be happy and at peace with who I was to my core, I just didn't know how to get there. It was time to call in a professional. I had placed so much of my well-being in the precarious hands of Tanner Bloomington for far too long. He was just one man, one imperfect human. He provided me with new building blocks, but I still wasn't an architect.

I scheduled my appointment for a week from that day and prayed that this heaviness would finally lighten soon. The road to stability is long and there are no shortcuts, no matter how creative we get. Now that I realized where my pain was coming from - my unwillingness to see positivity and accept happiness - confronting it head-on was the only way to get through it. I was finally ready to take that step towards better mental health and, in the words of my yoga instructor and creator of my favorite podcast, Dharma Drops Podcast, Rebecca Warfield "just go in sloppy."

13

Margie was pleased to have me sitting on her chic grey couch again. I wish I could've said the same. I felt defeated and optimistic all at once. Margie had won the battle, I was back on the couch, but I hoped I would win this cold war. If Margie was the bridge I had to cross to get to happiness, I could set my pride aside and suck it up for a couple months to get there.

She picked up right where she had left off and was discussing breathing exercises yet again. I decided to tell her about Tanner, the whole Tanner story. Finding him on a dating app, the bridge adventure, the movie theater - even our moonlit swim. After explaining to her that he would be leaving soon, she looked at me, with the most rueful expression on her face and said "Oh it's too bad that one couldn't have worked out. He was so good with you and seemed like a really good guy," and then asked me if I had done my breathing exercises during my panic attack in the movie theater. I was so pissed at her at that moment I didn't even know where to start. She had completely missed the point.

Unable to hold my tongue any longer, I said "Margie, I'm sorry, but I can't talk about deep breathing anymore, I just can't. I'm way past that kind of help." I don't know who was more shocked by my outburst. I couldn't believe I had just snapped at my therapist. It was rude but on the other hand it felt so *good.* I was finally speaking up and playing a part in bettering myself rather than standing in the corner and watching while other people try to do it for me. If nothing else, I had learned to take my mental health into my own hands. My disorder doesn't always fit the mold so my treatment shouldn't be any different and this admission was long overdue.

Margie clamped her mouth shut and stared at me a minute. After considering what I had said, she cocked her head to the side and replied, "Why do you feel that breathing exercises won't help you?" and this is where Margie lost me for good.

Margie, I thought, *if you must know, this is why "taking deeper breaths" will not be my saving grace - you have no idea how much I'm hurting because I don't have the tools to express my pain to you. That's not your fault, I downplay my emotions to everyone, and I laugh when I ask for help so how would you know that losing Tanner is turning me inside out?*

I've never been able to verbally express the feelings that swirl around in my head, mostly because I felt like I didn't deserve to feel them. I had a great childhood, I hadn't experienced any gruesome deaths like my friends had, and I wasn't addicted to drugs like my family members were, so I felt like I had no way to justify my sadness. And, for whatever reason, I couldn't say this to Margie because her pity would be more excruciating than physically saying the words aloud. I knew she would give me a concerned look and say: "Oh gosh, no! Of course, you can feel like that! All pain is pain." and I couldn't stand to hear it. It felt like everyone around me was going through a much more devastating trauma than I was. My sadness seemed obsolete in comparison to theirs, so I told myself I didn't deserve to feel it.

I didn't know this at the time, but I wasn't mad at Margie for simply telling me to breathe or for feeling sorry for me. I was mad at her for thinking I deserved to be happy when I felt so strongly that I didn't. I was harboring so much guilt inside my heart that even if Margie wanted to help me, she couldn't. I didn't believe I was worthy of resolving myself via her help as a therapist. I was fully convinced that I should have to live with that guilt for the rest of my life.

After Margie made her comment about wishing Tanner and I would have worked out, I knew I was paying my last copay to her young, freckled secretary that day. I went into that office with a vision of hope and absolution that was blocked out just minutes after I sat down. I told myself that therapy just wasn't for me and that I would be fine without it. I had sunk back down to my "I don't need anybody" way of thinking. I didn't need Margie, I didn't need Tanner, and I was going to be fine on my own. I always was.

I had been hiding in the back of my mind that tomorrow was the one-year anniversary of my friend's death. He was my ex's best friend and was killed suddenly in a motorcycle accident. I was petrified of this day. I was scared for so many reasons. I was scared to relive the trauma of that day; I was scared that I would have to do it alone now that I had just claimed to not need anyone. I was scared for my ex, that he wouldn't be able to handle it, and we would lose him too. I was afraid that this day would mean so many terrible things for so many great people. People that I no longer felt I had the right to reach out to. I had never told Tanner about that day, I didn't have the time with him that I thought I would, so he had no idea what I was going through.

I didn't sleep at all that night. I lay in bed waiting for my phone to buzz with news that something awful had happened, like it had so many other times before. Every time I would begin to drift off, I would be jolted awake by nightmare after nightmare. As I now felt I should, I suffered alone and in silence until I saw pastel pink colors bleed into the clouds, and spill in through my curtains. August 13th, 2018, was at the foot of my bed, waiting for me to open my eyes and stare into all its uncertainty. Meanwhile, behind my eyes, August 13th, 2017, was still clawing away at my memory. I wished so hard for Tanner to sense my pain from miles and miles away so he could swoop in and make it better like he always does. I thought I would be fine without anyone's help, but this was a horrible day to test my theory. My heart ached to be near Tanner, to feel free of the burden of my grief and enjoy the air that flowed through my lungs again.

14

J *ust keep counting. Count everything in this entire* *warehouse from truck decals to the hairs on your* *arms,* I thought to myself while doing voluntary inventory spot-counts in the shop that morning. It was the only activity I could do that would keep me busy until 5 p.m. when I could finally slough my grief off into the river. So far, nothing terrible had happened, but my anxiety clung to me like a human Otterbox. The hours passed so slowly that I was convinced I was trapped in a nightmare. I ran out of tasks in the shop quickly, as usual, which was why I was now "spot counting" every single item within a 3-mile radius until this merciless day was over.

After I had counted what must've been a thousand dusty harnesses, wheel chocks, and air filters, my lungs had had enough of the dust-filled air. I slid down the greasy wall of the dimly lit aisle of safety decals and took my phone out while I tried to catch my breath. Flashbacks from the day I lost my friend kept seeping into my memory despite my desperate attempt at sealing them off. I remembered the phone call, the 12-hour drive home, the funeral, all of it. I wanted it to stop; I wanted to feel better. I wanted to collapse into Tanner, and cry my eyes out. I always healed at his touch and our conversations took me so far from my worries that I often forgot they were there. I fantasized of a life where Tanner never had to leave, and my worries never found their way back home to me. I relished in that phantom life; the life where Tanner's face slept inches away from mine every night so that there was no room for worries and what-ifs between us.

I hadn't heard from Tanner since our last encounter and I knew he wasn't responding to my texts anymore, but I threw out one last line and typed, "Hi. I know things are weird but today is the one-year anniversary of my friend passing away and I could really use your company. Meet me for a walk later?" It felt desperate and embarrassing, but I was too tired to care. I was spiraling and couldn't muster the energy needed to slow it down.

He replied a few minutes later "Of course. I'll be there around 6." and I felt immediate relief wash over me. Things were fine; *I was going to be fine soon*, I thought to myself. I counted meaningless items in the stuffy old shop for 5 more hours, until all the numbers started to run together, and the accuracy of my counts plummeted dramatically. I punched my timecard and tried not to sprint-walk to my car that had been baking in the parking lot all day. On the way home, I realized I had no idea what I would say to Tanner. I hoped that I wouldn't have to say anything at all, and he would just be alone with me while I worked through my shit.

That afternoon, we met in our usual parking spots. I was dressed in jeans, black converse and my memorial T-shirt for my friend. Tanner was dressed in loose-fitting shorts, a neon cutoff, and abnormally, a snapback hat. It was a much douchier look than I was used to seeing on Tanner and all I could say was "Oh, you're wearing hats now?" with a deflated snicker. He replied flatly "I always wear hats." and feeling like I struck a nerve, I just nodded in agreement as if to say, "Sure you do."

Tanner and I began our usual route down the path towards the shit bridge and past the railroad bridge we had walked across ages ago (it had only been a month ago, but it felt like a year).

I was explaining to Tanner that it was a motorcycle accident that had taken my friend's life and it became harder and harder to make my words come up and out of my throat. Talking about how I had desperately called the local hospitals to see where they life-flighted him all those months ago made my throat close in on itself. I still remember the nurse telling me "I'm sorry ma'am, he's not here. He...may not have made it in" and how I didn't understand what she had meant until days later when a group of us were picking out pictures for the funeral.

A gust swept through the trees then, rattling their hanging branches, and I was brought back to the present. Tanner had let me get lost in the memory of that day but now, realizing I was back, he looked at me and smiled like he had something up his sleeve.

I was afraid of that smile. That smile had landed me on railroad tracks that bordered the clouds. I met his gaze and tentatively asked, "What? What are you concocting in your brain over there?" and he looked ahead at something I couldn't see. "I know what we're going to do today," he said, almost to himself. *Shit here we go again,* I thought as the pores on my hands and neck opened to allow the sweat to pour out. I paused before following Tanner any further. I wanted to say no at first as a knee-jerk reaction again, but this thrilling feeling was better than the hurt I felt from the memories racing through my mind.

This was the Tanner I had been missing and mourning. The Tanner whose eyes sparkled at the idea of an adventure and whose face exploded into a lopsided grin when an idea hit him like a brick wall. My body was on fire with adrenaline and raw infatuation again, like nothing had ever changed since our first night together under the stars. I didn't care about the danger anymore; all I wanted was this feeling of Tanner and Baleigh creating magic in the world around us again. I knew he was doing this to be a good friend and because he truly didn't want to see me in pain anymore, but I hoped he was doing it to relive our hay day too.

I caught up to Tanner, genuinely excited to hear where he was whisking me off to this time and said, "Fine. I'll try to keep an open mind." even though I knew I would follow him to the ends of the Earth at this point. *Careful what you wish for!*

We passed over the shit bridge, under the pavilion that was tucked beneath the train-track bridge and were now rounding the corner that led to the flat stretch of the bike trail. Rarely did we walk this far down the trail because it strays so far from the river and begins to become monotonous. Just as I was coming right around the bend, following the trail, Tanner veered off the path and into a thicket of bushes in the opposite direction. Confused, I stayed back as I called to him "Um, what are you doing? Did you see something shiny or something?" His head popped up from under a fallen tree and he waved for me to follow him. This felt like it was fifty shades of illegal, but I found myself ducking under the dead branches Tanner was holding up for me to pass under anyway. I started having PTSD flashbacks of Silvy and the alligator pond as we wade deeper into the brush.

Finally, I saw a clearing a few feet ahead of us and we pushed through the remaining weeds until we hit sunlight. Emerging from the tall weeds and cattails like lost Children of the Corn, a cold sweat broke out on my already-damp body at the sight of what was lying before us. It wasn't an open clearing after all, just more train tracks. Except this time, the tracks weren't vacant. There was a large freight train sleeping on the tracks in front of us and it dawned on me what Tanner had in mind now. *Oh hell no.*

My head whipped in his direction, all "open-mindedness" gone now, and I said to him "There's no way in hell. Absolutely not. You're a crazy person!"

He laughed, and his diabolical smile melted across his shattered poker face. I plopped my ass right there on the ground like a child to convey that he would have to drag me. I knew I was getting on top of this rattler, but I wasn't going to go easily. I was afraid, shaking in my damn converse, but I was getting up there. I just needed a little more convincing from Tanner before I took that leap of faith.

Expecting this reaction, Tanner said "Before you say no, I have also done this a million times, just like walking across the railroad bridge."

Did he just spend his days looking for local ways to accidentally die a painful death? I wondered. I shook my head childishly in opposition. He rolled his eyes at me and dropped down to the ground in one swift movement like he was about to start doing push-ups. Thinking that this was an odd time to get an arm-pump in I asked what he was doing.

"Just checking underneath the cars for hobos," he said.

I couldn't tell if he was kidding or not because he didn't laugh after he said it. He really had done this before. At least enough to know to check underneath the train for homeless people before climbing on. So that was mildly alarming.

Tanner reached for my hand, and I parroted, "Absolutely not." without budging. "Tanner, that train could start moving again at any minute and there's no way I would be able to get down fast enough!" I explained.

He looked at me, a little hurt, as he said, "You really think I would let that happen to you? I'm not going to let you get carried off to Pennsylvania on the back of a freight train." but I couldn't help thinking *How exactly would he be able to stop that from happening? Is there really an emergency brake in every car, Polar Express style?*

"Besides," he continued, "Would it really be so awful to get a free ride to anywhere else in the world other than your memories right now?" I knew he was kidding but I still had the urge to tell Tanner that he couldn't live his life thinking that Tom Hanks would be there to grab his sweater every time he slipped.

I stood up and gingerly approached the train car like it could awaken any minute at the snap of the branches under my sneakers. I felt like I was approaching a dormant volcano or the sick triceratops from Jurassic Park. I shifted my gaze slowly up to the peak of the car, following the haphazard ladder along the way, until finally landing my eyes on the metal roof. Tanner was behind me, hand on my back as he said, "I'll go up first so I can help you up." I was annoyed that he assumed I was going to do this incredibly reckless thing just because he wanted me to. On the other hand, I craved the thrill of not having to be me today. If I climbed that metal ladder, I wouldn't be acting as Baleigh anymore, but someone much braver. Someone who doesn't wake up every morning fearing the unknown. Tanner watched the emotions flick across my face like a slideshow and then began making his way up the ladder.

I watched like a toddler from the ground as he maneuvered his way up the ladder, over the rail, and onto the roof as gracefully as an ally cat. That only confirmed to me that there was no way I was going to make it up the ladder without falling and breaking my ankle on the way down. I shouted from the bottom, "There's no way I'm going to be able to do that! I'm way too clumsy!" and seeing the apprehension in my eyes, Tanner leaned over the railing and extended his arm down towards me. "I'll help you. You know I won't let you fall, it's really not that bad. It just looks scary because you're at the first step rather than the last." I knew he was referring to the ladder, but I pocketed that statement for a later time when Tanner wouldn't be next to me, and I needed the courage to make myself take a step forward onto one of life's many train cars.

Dropping my head so I could look at the first step on the ladder, I realized this step didn't look scary at all. Tanner called down to me, "Just take it one step at a time. Hand over hand, foot over foot, and when you make it to the top, I'll help you the rest of the way. You can do it. Come on." When I was a dumb drunken teenager and my friends would do crazy things like jump off of tall ledges into black water, I always held back and watched. I knew they were idiots, and I was afraid of everything. I don't know why Tanner had such a different influence on me, maybe because after everything we've been over, under, and through together, Tanner has always done his best to protect me, whether it be from himself or my own demons. I trusted him from day one with my whole heart to protect me. I knew he would never put me in harm's way.

I gripped the first wrung of the rusty ladder in my right hand, feeling for any give in the weathered metal. I reached my left hand to the step above that one and white-knuckled it as tightly as I could. Taking a deep breath (Margie would've been so proud), I made my feet follow my hands' pattern. I was moving robotically up the steep ladder without glancing down, one hand over the other, bird by bird, until finally there was no more of the ladder left to climb.

Finally, allowing my eyes to lift from the metal bars in my hands, I looked up to see that Tanner's face was just inches from mine. He was smiling, genuinely proud of me, as he said "See? I knew you could do it. You just get in your own way sometimes." I told him that now was not the time to teach me some lesson in courage as I was still dangling from the side of a train.

He laughed gently and grabbed my arms to help me up over the final barrier. As he was gripping my arms, I couldn't help playing in my head the scene in *Titanic* where Jack helps Rose over to safety after she attempts to jump from the ship. I'm swinging my left leg over the bar while my other foot balances carefully on the step below when I imagine Rose's shoe slipping on her dress right before she plummets down the side of the ship, Jack barely hanging onto her fluorescent arm. The panic leaves just as quickly as it came when I am safely placed next to Tanner on the roof of the train. I noticed that I was shaking with adrenaline and gratitude. I was so relieved that I hadn't slipped like poor Rose. Given the amount of sweat pooling in the palms of my hands, this was a miracle.

Once I was convinced that I was perched safely atop the roof; I took in the scene playing out around us. The panoramic view of the train tracks and the woods surrounding it was incredibly peaceful. There were no sounds of the river, pedestrian foot traffic, or children playing, just the sound of the weeds tickling each other, Tanner breathing softly and my heart thumping in my chest. I leaned my palms back against the cool metal roof to get more comfortable while I enjoyed the view and my left hand brushed against Tanner's. We both looked over to each other bashfully but neither of us took our hand away. Our eyes conveyed to each other a sense of understanding. We cared immensely for each other, and this was all we would ever be. Two people who cherished life and each other's lives but never got the timing right. In the background of my mind the words of Sam Smith's song "Palace" played in my mind, "Yeah, I know just what you're saying, and I regret ever complaining, about this heart and all its breaking. It was beauty we were making." He was right, real love is never a waste of time.

We watched the trees and the long cattails sway in the wind for quite some time together. The songs they whispered to each other were enchanting. I've always wondered what Tanner was thinking at that moment, and I'm regretful that I never asked. I assumed he was thinking about leaving and the journey he was going to embark on soon but in my heart of hearts I hoped he was thinking that he missed spending these little moments with me too. I wondered if he was imagining what his life would've been like had he stayed, if he was making the right choice. I wondered if he felt satisfied knowing that he was always exactly what I needed right when I needed it. I wondered if he thought it to be a coincidence that our paths crossed when they did or if he hoped in vain that I would still be here on top of this train waiting for his return six years from now.

It wasn't at all his responsibility, but he always made it a point to make me feel alive again right when he sensed that I was forgetting how to breathe, stifled by my own fear. I will always love him for taking that on when he didn't have to. I will always love everyone that has ever or will ever do that for me in my dark days.

The sun was sinking lower and painting the sky with beautiful milky shades of orange sorbet and pink cotton candy. I can still picture the hints of amber gleaming in Tanner's hair from the glare of the setting sun. I used my mental camera again to capture the moment for the scrapbook in my brain *click*. I wanted this moment to last a lifetime, to stretch it out for years and years, but Tanner broke the silence as he asked, "Do you feel better?" and I smiled as I said "Yes, much better now." and I meant that. A beautiful sunset spent on top of a locomotive with the one person who has ever made me feel at home in my own skin is more than I could have ever asked for on that day. It was everything I needed and more. I knew the beauty of this evening was not lost on Tanner either. He seemed pleased with my answer and said "Good. I'm glad your smile is back." he softly replied.

After we had our fill of adventure and splendor from our scenic hideout, we began the precarious climb back down the ladder. Tanner, of course going first, so he could help me with the dismount. Once we were both safely back on the ground, I thanked him for doing this for me, taking me to the train. As expected, he replied with "It was my pleasure" and a laugh. He trotted off back towards the Narnian thicket that led back to the paved path, but I paused, lingering on the tracks. I wasn't ready to leave the train that only minutes ago had gripped me with fear. I stared at the train, mesmerized by what I had just done. Tanner called for me to hurry up and I silently said my goodbyes to the rusted beast that had made this once unbearable day, one of the best days of my life.

I'm not blown away by grand gestures, fancy things, or far off destinations. It's the sunsets, the loved ones near, and the nature that surrounds me that make for a perfect day. A combination of all three in just one evening can move me to tears, and this one was doing just that. It was a day I will never forget. *I did something amazing today*, I thought. I conquered a fear, spent precious time with a man that my world revolved around the past three months, and I saw the beauty of the natural world from a once in a lifetime vantage point. It was bliss. It was what life was all about.

I couldn't tell why at the time, but this felt like a much larger goodbye than just a longing look back to a lifeless train. I couldn't make sense of why I was having such a hard time leaving the train that was not even a person, yet I had formed a human bond with. It was just an object, set there temporarily, that had taught me I don't have to necessarily be in motion to make great strides.

As I look back on this day now, I understand why I felt this sense of an internal chapter being closed around me that. It was the last time I ever saw Tanner again. As I try desperately to remember now what my last hug with him felt like, I am reminded of so many other hugs with loved ones that I hadn't realized at the time would be my last. I live my life these days by giving hugs that can be uncomfortably long and usually without apology. I never want to have to think to myself again, "I wish I wouldn't have been the first to let go." So now, like Rose Dewitt-Bukater, I'm the girl who never let's go.

15

That last great adventure was Tanner's fanfare that I never saw coming. He found every excuse under the sun to avoid coming down to the river with me after that night (working late, phone was dead, fell asleep, etc.) and I was incredibly hurt and upset about it. I couldn't begin to understand why he was even bothering to respond to my texts at all when he obviously wanted things to be over between us. Granted, weeks would pass by before he would respond to my messages, but he was still taking the time to answer. I knew it was time to let him go, for good this time, but I also knew this was hurting him as much as it was me. My heart ached to think that he felt he couldn't talk to me anymore. I was confused, sad, enraged and lonely all in the same breath.

One evening in late August, I let my temper get the best of me and I lashed out at Tanner for not being honest with me. I was on my way to my cousin's wedding with my mother and it had been days since I had last heard anything from him. Fed up, I fired off a text that read:

"I genuinely don't even know why you have a phone," and he replied (shockingly) almost immediately with, "Hey! Sorry I don't know why I have one either honestly. I might as well just throw it in the river."

I was not in the mood for jokes. He continued to tell me to have fun at the wedding tonight and that he would try to talk to me again before my 30th birthday. It was meant as a joke, but I was left fuming. *So,* I thought to myself, *He thought it was funny to keep blowing me off like this*? Well, that was all I needed to hear (or to assume, I should say).

At the time, I couldn't see that Tanner was consumed by his dreams and his own success. I couldn't see that he didn't know how to let me down. I couldn't see that he was desperately trying to put the needed space between us without hurting me anymore than he already had in the past. In my mind, he was just being selfish and insensitive, and he wished terribly that I would just leave him alone. Thanks, anxiety.

Anger, for me, is much easier to feel than sadness, thus making it my go-to emotion back then. I went on a full rampage as I typed up a long, ugly, rage-fueled text message that allowed all my built-up frustrations to break loose and claim the lives of every victim in its path. I told him how incredibly malicious it was to string someone along for so long with zero intentions of ever being with them. I called him a coward for not being able to end this for good since that was what he so badly wanted (again, my assumption, not his words). I went on to tell him to stop wasting my time if he was never going to be able to admit how deeply he cared for me. I spent the entire wedding checking my phone for his response, but it never came.

I can't blame him for never replying to that message. I wanted him to feel bad for hurting me and he did. Thinking that all he did was hurt me when he was in my life, he stopped everything right then and there. He completely stopped replying to my texts, going to the river, and taking my calls after that night. I had successfully pushed him as far away as I could before he had the chance to push me away first. I never considered that he wasn't going to end our relationship and friendship, and now I'll never know.

I had made my bed and now it was time to lie in it.

16

September blew in while the curtains closed on the summer of 2018. I was beginning my first semester at Kent State, and I felt incredibly nervous. I had applied while still living in North Carolina and was delighted to have been admitted on a transfer scholarship but also incredibly leery of this next step. I was convinced that the "4-year" classes would be ten times harder than the classes at the community college in North Carolina I had taken. Silvy was moving back down to Columbus, and I was having to make new friends for the first time since moving to Wilmington in 2015. Tanner, of course, hung around like a shadow in the back of my mind through every twist and turn that this month threw at me. I felt like an outline of who I was over the summer. The scars and silhouettes of love were there but past those solid lines, there was nothing but emptiness. My heart was sore and hollow now, so college was coming at the perfect time. I could dive headfirst into studying and researching to let my heart hibernate and recover.

By October, I hardly recognized the girl in

the pictures from my summer on the river. It felt like that entire season had been a dream. It had hit so hard and so fast that I was left reeling and staring back in awe. *Was Tanner a figment of my imagination?* I would find myself wondering. He was gone almost as quickly as he had appeared. In my spare moments in between classes, papers, and tests, these thoughts would float through my mind like smoke rings. I couldn't think about it anymore, it brought too much pain when I needed my brain back the most. School and good grades were important to me. I needed to keep my scholarships and grants and I couldn't do that with Tanner's face still so close to mine in my mind.

Somewhere along the way I decided I needed to make a clean break from Tanner if I ever wanted to move on. I deleted his text messages and his number from my phone. I was scrambling to erase every memory of him that I had and it all but broke my heart. He was really gone now, almost as if he had never existed to begin with. Like his hoodie never hung from my closet door. Like his fingertips never seared into the small of my back while we walked in the rain.

Around this time, I received news that reduced me to a puddle of happy tears.

"You're what?! How could you not tell me sooner?!" I screamed into my phone while lying on my futon one autumn afternoon. Squealing like a teenage girl at a Justin Bieber concert, I hopped off the futon yelling "Oh my God!! Oh my God!!"

Silvy was pregnant! I finally saw the clouds begin to part and reveal the warmth I'd been craving for months. This was one of the happiest moments of my entire life. I had never had any baby siblings, nor nieces and nephews, so I was ecstatic to finally have a baby in my life. I already loved her more than I could explain in words (I knew immediately it was a girl) and for the next eight months I picked out pink bows, pregnancy pillows and stuffed hedgehogs every second of free time I could find.

After the initial shock of hearing my best friend say, "I'm due in June," my first thought was that I wanted to tell Tanner because I knew he would be excited not just for me, but for Silvy too. Realizing that there was no Tanner to tell everything to, neither my fears nor my passions, my heart broke all over again.

He loved kids. He would've shared my giddy smile like he used to when I told him of things that lit my heart up from the inside. I hadn't finished crying my happy tears before my heartbroken tears began to bleed into them. I thought I was doing so well without Tanner but what I realized now was that I had only temporarily numbed myself. I had been refusing to think of him or the memories we made until I was forced to feel these new intense emotions for the baby. With new emotions always comes the old ones I had desperately tried to bury.

All I could feel then was guilt for my sadness. This was one of the happiest moments life had to offer and yet here I was, still mourning my summer romance. I decided I needed to try more of the therapy techniques I had learned over the years to kick this whole "moving on" thing into high gear. So, I began writing again, and not just lengthy research papers.

Despite the chilly air that had crept into Northeast Ohio, I started to write letters to Tanner almost every day down by the river. This was supposed to be a way to get all my thoughts and feelings out so I could be more present in my everyday life. In the beginning, writing these letters was enthralling. I told Tanner all about Silvy's baby coming in just eight months, how I knew without a doubt, the baby would be a little blonde-haired version of Silvy, how my new college classes were going, the changes that had happened around the hike-and-bike trail and how sorry I was for the way things ended between us. I let everything out of my heart and onto the paper like poison. I just wanted it out of me so I could live my life again.

As productive as these letters were, they always ended the same way. My last sentence was almost always, "The river misses you terribly." I was too prideful to admit that it was me who truly missed him, even in a letter that only I would ever read. However, I did genuinely believe the river missed him just as much as I did. Since he had stopped coming, the water had grown dark and cold, the leaves began to die, and our ledge had been covered in genitalia graffiti. Of course, I knew most of these changes were due to the shift in seasons and influx of college kids, but I'd never seen the trail in the fall and winter months, so this change felt heightened to me. Overdramatized even, as a direct result of Tanner's absence.

As I walked the trails alone, I began noticing things I'd never seen before. I would find myself wondering things like, *"Has that bench always been rotted out?"* and *"Has a homeless man always slept under the bench in the gazebo?"* With Tanner gone, the river was losing its magic and the trees had stopped whispering their songs in the breeze. It slowly began to look like an ordinary public park as its colors faded to grey.

After I had compiled almost an entire notebook of unsent letters for Tanner, I lit a bonfire in my backyard, cracked open a Sam Adams and began ripping the pages out of the notebook one by one. I was still completely heartbroken and now I had all these stupid letters to prove it. Sprawled out in my lawn chair, I watched them all burn in that fire until all that was left was the metal spiral that once held them all together. I watched the flames blister each word I had poured out from my heart until I was convinced that my heart itself was on fire now, melting the bones in my ribcage.

Swilling my beer, I watched as the ashes of my greatest love story floated up into the sky above me until they disappeared completely.

While I doused the smoldering flames with the garden hose later that night, I hoped that wherever Tanner was now, the ashes had reached him. I hoped the smoke had curled in through his open bedroom window and whispered my apologies into his ear. I willed my love for him to be painted in the bonfire flames across the matte black sky. Before finally going inside to my bed, I prayed for the first time in months. I asked God to take care of Tanner and lead him to his peace, whatever that was to him. I also asked God to help me find my own peace without Tanner next to me. *Please don't let that be it for me*, I plead silently to the stars.

17

Utilizing everything that I learned that summer, I began to fully live my life again. A life without Tanner, but a life nonetheless. I knew he was right in doing what he did. I needed to let go and move on. It was difficult adjusting to a life where I didn't have Tanner to talk to when I was feeling low, but I always carried him with me. The connection and bond we formed was much larger than the two of us, whether we wanted to admit it or not.

My first semester at Kent State was hard, but I maintained a 3.5 GPA and became enthralled with my Communication Studies classes regardless of the intensity of the workload. I was proud and incredibly shocked with my success in these classes. I thought for sure I'd be struggling to keep up, but I excelled despite myself. I even dabbled in dating again, but traces of Tanner would still surface around this town that was once ours when I was least expecting it. This made it hard for my heart to ever be fully present in any dating encounter. All the potential suitors fell so terribly short compared to what my heart had in mind. They paled in comparison to my tall dark and tattooed toe-shoe-wearing Romeo.

The following summer (summer of 2019), I was scrolling through my Facebook feed when I decided to go through my "People you may know" suggestions on a boring Friday night. The things I did to avoid writing a paper in my college days never ceased to amaze me. While mindlessly scrolling through all my friends' parents, old high school teachers and people I knew a lot about but had never actually met, I stopped dead on a woman's profile picture. Tanner's face was staring back at me from the screen. Well to be exact, it was a bulkier, more mature, and Navy uniform-clad version of Tanner. I concluded that it must be his mother's profile, despite the different last names. I clicked to enlarge the picture to be sure it was really him and sure enough, there was the crooked smile gleaming at the lens of the camera.

He made it, I thought to myself. He had made it into the Navy after all. Tears rolled down my face with nothing but sheer pride for him. His smile was bashful, but I could see that he was happy, and what more could I want for him? I was so thankful to have stumbled upon that picture of him in his crisp-white uniform. It was the closure that I hadn't realized I so desperately needed. There was peace in knowing that we were both making our dreams come true.

18

My days on campus pushed on. I was still closing the door on Tanner when I noticed that my walks along the river were becoming painful. By November I was finding that I couldn't sit through my lectures or even long movies anymore. I could no longer workout or go for runs, and I couldn't sleep through the night due to my knee pain. Finally, when I couldn't stand it any longer, I made the decision to see a doctor. He did all the X-rays and paperwork necessary to diagnose me with Chondromalacia Patellae and then gave me the unfortunate news that it would require years of physical therapy to fix and maintain the pain unless I wanted to have surgery.

During my first five sessions in PT, I had an amazing physical therapist named Denise and she took great care of me. We formed a bond, and I grew accustomed to her dry humor.

At my sixth appointment, Denise told me that she was passing me onto her assistant, Angela, because her work here was done, and she had other people who needed her help. I was distraught but I trusted that her assistant would help me just as much as she had. Denise introduced me to Angela and the first thing I noticed was her Pittsburgh Steelers lanyard and, without meaning to, I immediately judged her. A Cleveland Browns girl never trusts a Steelers fan that lives in Northeast Ohio. It's just not natural.

Angela was much tougher on me than Denise had been. Eventually, I learned to match her tone and we bonded over tattoos (her daughters had them too) and our love of animals. She was tough but it turned out that's what I had needed to strengthen my legs past what Denise had started for me. Angela grew on me, and I was sad to leave her when my two months of physical therapy were over. I felt so close to her, and I respected her immensely. I felt like I knew her, or I had met her before, but I couldn't quite place it.

My break from PT didn't last long though; I was back for more therapy a little less than a year later when I found myself having to leave lectures early again because of my knee pain. Expecting to be rematched with Angela for physical therapy, I was sad to see a middle-aged man calling my name in the waiting room of the PT office. I followed him back to the exam room and walked laps back and forth yet again so he could study my gait like Denise had done. During one of these laps, I caught a glimpse of Angela helping an elderly woman on the stationary bikes and I waved to her. She waved back and smiled at me, and I was delighted to see that she remembered me.

Randy, my new physical therapist, led me over to the stationary bikes to get my knees warmed up for today's exercises and I plopped down on my usual bike. I had just begun to pedal when I saw Angela saunter over out of the corner of my eye. We exchanged small-talks and asked how the other was doing since it had been a while since we had last seen each other. Angela told me she had gotten married, and I happily congratulated her. I asked her about her new hubby, and she told me that he worked for a landscaping company not far from here. When she said the name of the company, my foot jarringly slipped off the flimsy pedal.

"I'm sorry, what did you say your husband's name was again?" I sputtered as I attempted to find the pedal with my foot again. "Oh, his name is Tanner. Tanner Bloomington, why?" I stopped pedaling entirely and stared up at Angela in shock. I was catching flies.

At first, for a split second, I thought she had married *my* Tanner until I remembered he was a Junior and that his father was Tanner Bloomington Senior. "Oh, no reason!" I exclaimed as I tried to cover up my embarrassment, "I just knew a Tanner Bloomington that worked for that company too." I tried to brush that detail off nonchalantly, but Angela's eyes lit up as she said "Oh you must mean

Tanny! That's my step-son!" I hoped I didn't look too relieved or terrified or whatever I was feeling at that moment.

As I watched in horror, Angela turned to Randy and said "Did you hear that?! Baleigh here knows my Tanny!" then turning back to me she added, "How do you know Tanny?"

Tanny. His family called him Tanny; I never knew that. By now I was sure my entire face had gone white, and I was scrambling to make my mouth and brain work simultaneously. I was completely thrown off guard and had no idea how to explain how I knew Tanner. *How did I know Tanner?* Stammering, I said, "Oh we dated very briefly a couple summers ago. How is he doing anyway?" No big deal! Totally normal question to ask! I began to sweat profusely.

I watched Angela digest this information and process it carefully before answering me. With slightly less enthusiasm (Or maybe I imagined that?), she said, "He's doing really well." and then shakily adding, "He's actually in town right now!" I willed myself not to display my reaction on my face, and this was no easy feat for me. *Of course, he is,* I thought. My world shifted. Tanner was close by again. How did I feel about that?

"Oh, that's great! I'm sure he misses being home with you guys," I said, knowing damn well he didn't care much for his father and stepmother's company.

Angela nodded and agreed that yes, he missed being home and was enjoying his time with his family. There was a pause and then she asked "Do you want me to tell him I bumped into you? I'd love to rag on him and tell him I met one of his old flames!" I laughed because this was something I would do to my own child but internally, I was frothing with nausea at the thought of Tanner knowing I knew his stepmother. "Sure, I bet he would love that!" I replied jokingly with a painfully forced laugh. I wondered if he would in fact *love* that or if he would file a restraining order against me for stalking his family.

Angela tossed an "I'll be sure to embarrass him for you!" over her shoulder as she headed back to her patient. I laughed nervously at myself, not knowing what I had or hadn't just done. I wondered if Tanner would reach out to me now or if Angela would forget to tell him. I wondered if he would even care. Maybe he would say "Baleigh? Baleigh who?"

After my PT session, I slipped on my puffy winter coat and exited through the automatic doors in a frenzy. Once I reached the safety of my car, I allowed myself to process the fact that I had been hanging out with Tanner's stepmom for two months. *Holy shit that was his stepmom the entire time?!* I combed over all our past conversations to make sure I hadn't revealed too much about myself and to see if she had mentioned anything about Tanner that I didn't pick up on earlier. Nothing stuck out to me, but I knew my memory played tricks on me often so all I could think of was all the possibly incriminating things I had mentioned to her during our sessions. Tanner was back though; she had mentioned that he was home on leave. I became hyper aware of my surroundings on my drive home from the doctor's office; *He could be anywhere,* I found myself thinking. I wasn't sure how that made me feel but I missed two turns that I had taken a million times on my way home that day.

Once I got home, I decided to take a catnap before my afternoon class. I remember dreaming of the river and chasing a man that must've been Tanner. I couldn't seem to catch up to him, no matter what shortcut I took or how fast I ran through the trees, he was always just out of my reach.

The next morning, I had a voicemail from the physical therapist's office saying that they were suspending all my future appointments indefinitely due to COVID-19 concerns. I never saw Angela again and I never got to hear Tanner's reaction to his stepmom meeting me. I'll never know if he ran screaming from the dinner table or if he excused himself to go lie down and listen to Wildflower on repeat. I'll always wonder how that conversation went.

19

There was a time when I fully believed that I would never be able to love another man again. I was convinced that there would never be a touch that melted me to my core like Tanner's had. There was an even longer period when I believed that love just wasn't meant for me. I thought that love wasn't for independent, confrontational and strong-willed women like myself. Love was for those doe-eyed girls who could bake a casserole with their eyes closed and had handwriting that was so beautiful that people would pay for it to be emblazoned onto their stationary. I told myself these lies that I was too hard to love because every cell in my body defensively fought to push people away before they could hurt me.

During the summer of 2020, when the rest of the world around me seemed to be dying, I did manage to love again. While this love unfortunately was also not mine to keep, it gave me hope. I knew in my heart that Tanner was never coming back, so to know that my heart could love someone else again, revived my hope for a love of my very own. A love that I could keep all for myself without any doubts or fear of abandonment. A love that I knew I deserved. This towering, thin, and kind-hearted man that I found myself falling in love with on the banks of a murky lake with our fishing poles positioned towards the dirt and our lines tight across the channel, was also not the one for me. However, he was the one to help me see there was more for me out there and that I could allow another man to hold my heart in their hands.

While I fell for this new man, I still knew in the back of my mind that I will always love Tanner and he will always have a piece of me with him that I can never get back. And that's okay. That doesn't mean my story ended on top of that train in late August of 2018. Love is all around me, I just have to allow myself to see it. It's hard to find love when you're spending all your time telling yourself you don't deserve it.

In more ways than he could ever know, Tanner saved me. He helped me to see all the beauty this world has to offer; beauty that I was so often taking for granted. The way he painted the picture of life for me made it impossible not to be excited to live again. The magic and wonder of everyday life had become so dormant in me that I had forgotten what it truly meant to be alive. Tanner lived this life so beautifully that it could make anyone question how much of their own life they had been wasting on trivial matters. I know he still loves the trees, greets the river and thanks the clouds. Gratitude oozes from every pore on his effortlessly tanned face.

Without noticing, I had become the person who lost track of time watching rivers run and clouds pass. I was so grateful for all the people that I loved dearly and the blossoming environment that surrounded me every day that I felt I could burst with love. I began inhaling endless possibilities and exhaling irrational fears that had been clinging to me for months and months. The world became a place I yearned to explore again. My fear and anxiety began to slip from my body like a silk robe to the ground, leaving behind my naked soul, exposed to the sun.

Along the rocky ledges of the river, on top of that cement rock wall, high above the river on those train tracks, and dangling from the back of that parked train, I fell in love. With Tanner, with life and finally, with *myself*.

EPILOGUE

From the comfort of my Grandpa's old recliner that now sits in my mom's spare bedroom, I have drained my entire heart into these blank pages. It's 2021 now, three years since I met Tanner. Three years since I've seen his face or held his hand. Three years since his phone number has feathered across the screen of my iPhone.

The truth is this story was so much harder to tell than I expected that I stopped writing this book many times. Sometimes, I was just frustrated with the inner turmoil that comes with editing your story and other times it was due to the emotional difficulties associated with working full-time during a global pandemic. However, the first time I stopped writing was because I came face-to-screen with Tanner's girlfriend about halfway through writing my rough draft. Yeah. His Girlfriend. With a capital G.

I had gone back to Tanner's mother's Facebook page to make sure I was accurately describing the picture of him in his Navy uniform, when I was met with a new profile picture of Tanner. Only this time he was accompanied by presumedly, his sister and another woman that I didn't recognize. Her smile was enchanting, and her slight frame was infuriating. Tanner loved her; I could see that in their closeness. After looking over her profile briefly it was clear that they were together.

In that instant, I felt like my story no longer mattered. This love story I had spent months writing was no longer mine to tell; it was hers. Tanner's heart didn't belong to me and with that came the wave of doubt. I felt that it was a lie and that I had built up this fairytale in my head that never happened, or that had only happened to me. I moved on because I had to, he moved on because he wanted to and that broke me, again.

I was so embarrassed. It was apparent now that it wasn't his lack of time or his impending future in the military that had cut our ties-it was me. He just hadn't wanted to be with me. I wondered at what point he decided this and how I had missed it. I realized this woman was his previous ex-girlfriend and it comforted me to know that maybe she just offered a sense of familiarity that I couldn't offer him. Whatever the reason was, I had to accept that it had nothing to do with me. Tanner had been long gone and what he did with his time now was not something I had the right to think I was a part of anymore.

After a few days of tears and intense meditation, I decided that my story did still matter. Tanner's girlfriend has her own story of Tanner but this one, *At Home with the Weeds,* was mine and no one could ever take that from me. Maybe one day she'll tell hers too and we'll have tequila shots in a sticky bar about it. Maybe she'll fling poop at my head, who knows. I don't believe they are together anymore and while that should bring me relief, it doesn't. I feel for her. Whether it was her decision or not, I know how hard it is to lose Tanner and I wouldn't wish that on any other woman. The wind can't be held.

The vine-swing that Tanner and I sat on after our first date was destroyed during a particularly devastating summer storm and a couple new wooden planks have been installed along the shit-bridge but other than that, the trail remains the same. My left hand still instinctively falls to my side, with my five fingers spreading wide, like it did years ago, in search of Tanner's hand. In the summer, the warm air comforts my empty grasp, and the sunshine palms my pale cheeks like Tanner used to when he kissed me. I still feel him in the bark of every tree and the whistle of every passing train. I carry his slanted smile, tucked deep inside the pockets of my heart, around every familiar turn.

While my setting has not changed, all my

characters have. By that I mean, there have been new men and even newer friends. In June of 2019, Silvy gave birth to her beautiful little baby girl, who is quintessentially her mini-me. She was a perfect reimagination of the sweet baby girl I dreamt about since the day I learned of her existence. With her iridescent-blond waves of thin hair and brilliant blue-green eyes, she is the spitting image of her mother. For the first year of her life, Silvy's baby had one blue eye and one brown eye but eventually she grew into her mother's blue eyes. Silvy will tell you, to this day, that her eyes are green, but I am putting it on record right now, in this book, that they are 100% blue. That's actually the real reason why I wrote this book. Just kidding!

Unfortunately, after Silvy had her baby, we began to drift apart. Motherhood was hard for her, and I was no longer someone she could relate to or confide in. I was there for her, and I visited her down in Columbus from time to time, but the glaring differences grew harder and harder to adapt to with each visit. It was heartbreaking to look at her daughter, who I had grown to love as a niece, and know that soon she would have no idea who I was or that I had once been a huge part of her tiny life.

By 2020, Silvy and I rarely spoke to each other, and the visits only happened once every couple of months if at all. When I sat next to her, I didn't know who she was, and I knew she no longer knew me either. I will always love Silvy and be eternally grateful for the ten years of best friendship we shared, but she is where she was meant to be now and so am I. Hopefully those two places will one day intersect again but until that time comes, I will continue to love and support her from the distance we created together.

As the saying goes, when one door closes another one opens, and many friendship doors opened for me after Silvy's closed. Each one taught me confidence, autonomy, and gratitude. I had forgiven my former self for her mistakes and now I was letting my body reflect that change of mindset to the world. I paid off my student loans, bought a new car, and started seeing a chiropractor (it doesn't sound like much, but seeing a chiro really changes your life when you work a desk-job). I loved looking in the mirror. I loved the friend that I was to the ones that I loved the most.

I look around at all the incredible people surrounding and supporting me and I am blinded with gratitude.

I know that what is meant for me will find me, or in this case, find me again. I just pray that one day my heart lands in the hands of a man that would give anything to protect it, whether that man is Tanner or not, I know I deserve that now. I wish him nothing but all the love in the world and each time I catch the heavy scent of the river on the breeze, I'll think of him and know that he's still out there, swirling around in the world with his toe-shoes on.

With all the unconditional love enveloping me now, I can unveil a new and improved version of myself that I can finally be proud of and comfortable with. I am at home with myself for the first time in my life and that freedom is dizzying at times. I am in control of my anxiety; it now bows down to me rather than vice versa. I now have the tools I've always had but never understood how to utilize to do the one thing I have fantasized about doing since childhood. I'm ready to grab the one thing in my closet of dreams that I could always see on the highest shelf but could never quite reach. And I know exactly what the title will be.

ACKNOWLEDGE-MENTS

The first person I have to thank for this book coming to fruition is my mother, of course. In everything that I've ever done, I've had my mom there to help me. She's gotten me out of every sticky situation that I've found myself in and supported every crazy dream I've ever had (and there have been many). From wanting to go to Yale after watching Gilmore Girls for the first time, to picking up and moving to the coast of North Carolina with only $800 and a cat to my name, and finally to going back to college four times, she helped me make it all possible and this book was no different.

My mother introduced me to my love of reading and writing at a young age. As a single mom, the library was a close friend of hers. I loved all the puppets, the puzzles, and of course, the books. I loved books long before I could read and once, I had mastered reading, I couldn't wait to begin writing. My mom was at all my Power of the Pen competitions, and I could only imagine that was the most boring thing to spectate. Our shared love of reading and in books in general has always been something that's tied us together. My mom is my entire life, and I would be nothing without her. Thank you for everything Mom, love you more.

Going along with my mom, I also want to thank my grandparents. My mom's parents were like a bonus set of parents for me. My grandpa has been my father-figure since I was born. It was hard growing up as the only girl who didn't have a father, but he did everything in his power to ease that burden for me. He taught me how to fish, cheered me on at my softball games, and helped me buy my first car, and he loved every minute of it. My grandpa is the best "father" I could've ever asked for and I love him dearly for it.

My grandmother had the unfortunate task of watching me while my mom worked full-time as an ER nurse. To keep me occupied, my grandma would read with me. I am willing to bet that there's nobody else in the world who has read more books than my grandmother. She instilled in me my love for reading at a young age and it stayed with me all throughout my adult life. My grandmother volunteered at multiple different libraries for many years because she loved to be surrounded by books and other people that adored literature as much as she did. She was also the one who would drive me back and forth to my first job, which was volunteering at the local library. Yes, that is three generations (and possibly more) of Bognar women working at the library- one of us was bound (pun intended) to become an author eventually! My grandmother is my biggest fan, and no one is ever as happy to see me as she is. She melts my heart, and I will cherish our memories endlessly.

In the spirit of keeping, it in the family, I also have to thank my little cousin Mikey. Or, more professionally, my full-grown adult cousin Michael Fletcher. With a background in graphic design from THE Ohio State University, Mikey designed my beautiful book cover. He was also one of my biggest fans during the writing process. I'll never forget what he said to me when I asked him to help me design the cover for At Home with the Weeds; "Don't let anyone talk you out of doing this, especially yourself". This became my mantra for the next seven months. I can never thank him enough for *all* of his help, on and off the cover.

Also in the cousin family, I have to acknowledge the lovely and talented Kelly Samardak. Not only is she my personal photographer, but she is also my hilarious partner in crime. Kelly was the first person that I told when I decided to write this book because I knew she would be as excited as I was. This little lady supports me better than my favorite bra. To my Trish Garbago, my Hulu nerd, and my soul sister, I am forever grateful for your knowledge, guidance, and Hi-jinks. Without your support and shared love of my dreams coming true, I would be mush. I love you always!

Now for the non-family members:

My developmental editor who took my tip of the iceberg and turned into the giant glistening monster it is now, Margay Dean. As a developmental editor will do, Margay pushed me past the limits I had set for myself to make this book be everything that it could be. Her revisions were amazing and so spot on, I couldn't thank her more for saving this book that was almost a published disorganized diary entry. She challenged me to dig deep down into the ugly parts of my brain and it really brought this book to life. I am eternally grateful for your dedication to improving my writing.

I'm also throwing in a shameless plug to my amazing tattoo artist. Joe Rafferty has been my pal since back in the day. From doing tatties in his kitchen to watching him become the well sought-after manager at his tattoo shop, we've been through it all. He is the mastermind behind my watercolor half-sleeve and the watercolor wildflower tattoo that reads "She's at home with the weeds" amount a few other tattoos of mine. His wildflower tattoo that he did on my left arm inspired the cover (and clearly the title) of this book. Go get some work done from him at War Horse Ink in Kent, Ohio. Love you homie!

I had to save my first editor for last because I knew I was going to bawl like a baby when I wrote this acknowledgement. Chelsey Church. I don't even know where to start. Chelsey frickin Church: editing master, grammar and punctuation queen, bad ass mother of two, honesty angel, and inspiring ass bitch. Chelsey was the only person to read the first draft of this book and to read each chapter in real time as I spewed them out. *And she loved them.* A real-life editor was *liking* what I was writing, and I genuinely didn't know how to take in that information. So naturally I cried. And then I cried 8 more times.

Chelsey, thank you for looking into the depths of my soul and editing its punctuation flawlessly. More importantly though, thank you for giving me that light at the end of the tunnel I had no idea I had been desperately searching for. Having a pro like yourself believe in my dreams was the most incredible feeling I've ever experienced and our bond that we created during this process is something I will never forget. Thank you thank you thank you. For everything.

ABOUT THE AUTHOR

Baleigh Bognar

Baleigh Bognar can usually be found with her nose in a book. Now, she can finally be found with her nose in her own book.

When she's not writing, Baleigh enjoys hiking with her puppy, practicing yoga, and trying to learn to like IPA's. Baleigh lives in Stow, Ohio with her two cats, Sadie and Huey, and her new puppy, Jovi.

She has been competing in short-story competitions and writing leisurely since elementary school and always dreamt of publishing her own story. After completing her degree in Communication Studies from Kent State University, she decided to write and self-publish her debut memoir, At Home with the Weeds.

Made in United States
North Haven, CT
22 March 2022

17410372R00141